RYA Electrics Handbook

by Andrew Simpson

Illustrations by the Author

© Andrew Simpson 2009

First Published 2009

The Royal Yachting Association

RYA House, Ensign Way, Hamble
Southampton SO31 4YA

Tel: 0845 345 0400

Fax: 0845 345 0329

E-mail: publications@rya.org.uk

Web: www.rya.org.uk

ISBN: 978-1906-435-240

RYA Order Code: G67

Totally Chlorine
Free

Sustainable
Forests

A CIP record of this book is available from the British Library.

Note: While all reasonable care had been taken in the preparation of this book, the publisher takes no responsibility for the use of the methods or products or contracts described in the book.

Cover Design: Pete Galvin

Typesetting and Design: Kevin Slater

Proofreading and indexing: Alan Thatcher

Printed in China through World Print

FOREWORD

There can be few more unsettling experiences than mechanical problems at sea: the helpless feeling as you rack your brains for some kind of solution while drifting miles away from any help can be frustrating to say the least.

This brings us to electrics, which have become so fundamental to the modern boat that the thought of electrical failure can send a shudder down the spine of even the most experience mariner. We rely on our electrics to start the motor, illuminate the boat at night and power our many navigational gizmos.

In the most extreme cases, some modern engines rely on electronics not only to start, but also to keep them running.

In my role as director of Sea Start marine breakdown services, I have spent much of the past couple of decades repairing many different boats and I can confidently say that many of these problems have originated from dodgy electrics whether it be poor installation or bad upkeep.

This is where this book comes to the fore; providing a comprehensive guide to all aspects of marine electrics and providing you with the knowledge to remedy many problems before they disrupt your boating.
I hope you enjoy reading this book as much as I did. Trust me; it could save you a lot of trouble further down the line.

Nick Eales

Sea Start

www.seastart.co.uk

INTRODUCTION

What exactly is electricity? Its marvels are all around us, just a flick of a switch away, but the outward signs of its existence tell us almost nothing about the invisible forces at work. For some the practical outcomes are sufficient. If the lights turn on, the radio squawks and beverages chill in the fridge, who cares how it happens?

Few boat owners would have trouble answering that question. As our reliance on electrical systems increases, it's reassuring to have a good understanding of what's going on around us. At least then we can anticipate where problems might occur and guard against them to minimise the risk of failures. Moreover, when things do go wrong, we will have a valuable insight into how they may be put right – even if we may not be able to do the work ourselves. For clearly, in these days of micro-technology, with many electrical components sealed and inaccessible, there's a limit to what we can tinker with.

But, with mounting complexity, the need to get the fundamentals right has become more important than ever before. The basic circuitry and its immediate ancillaries are the foundations upon which all the rest depends. Unfortunately, many older boats are now struggling with electrical burdens never imagined when their systems were conceived. The process of upgrading such systems starts with acquiring some knowledge of the principles involved.

And that's what this book is all about.

Andrew Simpson

Acknowledgements: Many friends and experts have been generous with their time and expertise in the production of this book. I would particularly like to thank Andrew Hurrell BSc (Hons), PhD and Alan Robertson IEEET(T.Eng), CEI–AMBIM who were kind enough to read the manuscript and put me right on some of the finer points.

CONTENTS

CHAPTER 1

BASIC THEORY

A popular way to demonstrate electrical characteristics is to make comparisons with water flowing through a plumbing system – a 'hydraulic analogy' as it's sometimes called. Conveniently for us, even some of the terminology is identical: 'flow' and 'current' mean much the same in either camp, even 'eddies' in obscurer contexts, and 'valves' and 'condensers' are to be found in both disciplines. And, for the most part, the analogy is very useful – so useful, indeed, that we shall be giving it an airing within the very next few pages.

But at the most elemental level the comparison falls down. Water is a substance, tangible and visible. Given a transparent pipe, you can see it flowing. Electricity, on the other hand, works unseen and has some astonishing qualities. It will pass through highly conductive materials almost without hindrance, and usually without disturbing the material or changing its appearance or nature. So, what exactly is this stuff and how does it perform these tricks?

One dictionary describes electricity as 'the manifestation of a form of energy associated with the movement of charged particles'. Well, that's certainly an accurate definition but it hardly throws open the window to a full understanding of the issue. So, let's fill in some of the details.

Looking into atoms

The phrase 'charged particles' refers to those that go to make up atoms (Figure 1:1). At the heart of each atom is a dense nucleus consisting of electrically neutral neutrons and positively charged protons. All but a miniscule scrap of an atom's mass is in the nucleus. Orbiting the nucleus are a number of tiny, almost weightless electrons. These carry a negative electrical charge and collectively balance the positive charge of the nucleus, thereby leaving the atom electrically neutral as a whole. If it lost or gained an electron the atom's neutrality would be compromised and it would become an 'ion' – something we will be looking at later.

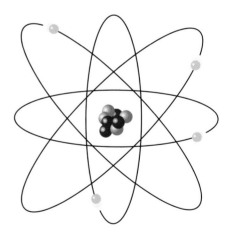

Figure 1:1

Figure 1:2 opposite shows a flattened representation of an atom. Of course, in real life it would be three dimensional and those concentric orbits can be thought of as nesting 'shells', one inside the other like the skins on an onion and not necessarily spherical. This atom has an 'atomic number' of 29, meaning it has 29 protons and 29 electrons (and, incidentally, 34 neutrons which for our purposes we can ignore). Note the outer shell which is occupied by a single electron. This vulnerable orphan of the atomic world is known as a 'valence' electron and requires only a small amount of energy to nudge it free from its attraction to its nucleus.

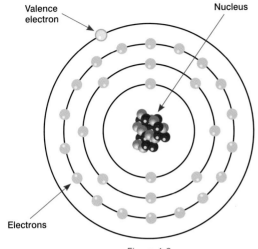

Valence electron

Nucleus

Electrons

Figure 1:2

The atom we are looking at is copper – a metallic element widely used as a conductor, hence its choice as our example. And the electron's break for freedom when it willingly occurs is electrical energy. All elements that enthusiastically shed electrons are conductors. Some better than others. Those that hold fast to their electrons are insulators.

So, an electrical current is a sort of atomic bucket chain where the atoms don't move but the electrons are passed from atom to atom (Figure 1:3). The knock-on effect is almost instantaneous and – unlike water in a pipe – isn't measured by the progress of a single particle. Push one extra pea into the end of a fully loaded peashooter and another will instantly pop out of the other end, despite the fact that the intruder pea has only just started its journey (Figure 1:4). Incidentally – and you might think illogically – because electrons are negatively charged, their actual movement is against the flow of the current as we know it.

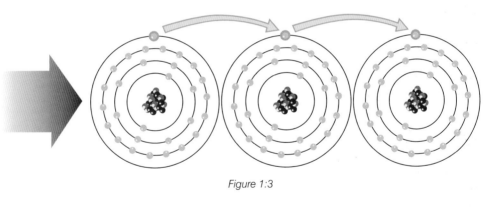

Figure 1:3

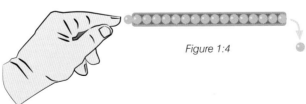

Figure 1:4

I'll leave you to ponder that (actually it's because electric currents were identified before we had discovered electrons) but, a more important fact to us is that all electrons are the same. If, say, you were unfortunate enough to become part of a circuit, the current would not stop because it's run out of conventional conductor. It simply wouldn't know the difference. The electrons within your body are interchangeable with those in the live cable and will cheerfully take up the baton, allowing the current to be conducted through you – possibly with lethal results. (See page 53)

TERMS AND DEFINITIONS

It's now time to come to grips with some essential terminology. Without it there can be no deeper understanding of the subject.

Note that those wayward electrons on the previous page weren't bounding from atom to atom spontaneously. They were being pushed by an outside force. This is aptly known as an 'electromotive force' (or EMF) and its strength is expressed in 'volts' (after Alessandro Volta, inventor of the first battery). Its designated symbol is 'V'. The higher the number the stronger the force.

A VOLT can be thought of as a unit of electrical force.

Now, if it were possible to be a bystander counting those electrons as they passed, you would get some idea as to how much current was flowing. The drawing shows them in single file – feeble without a doubt. But what if they marched by a hundred abreast? Or perhaps a thousand

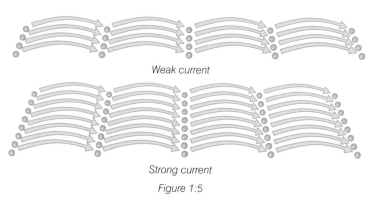

Weak current

Strong current

Figure 1:5

… or maybe several million? Clearly, the more numerous the electrons the greater the current. And the size of that current is expressed in 'amperes' (named after the French physicist André-Marie Ampère and usually shortened to 'amps'). Its symbol is 'A' but, for reasons that will become clear later, it's represented in equations by the letter 'I'.

An AMPERE is the unit of electrical current.

Our practical interest in these matters will eventually lead us to wonder how useful any current will be – i.e. how much work it will do; its power. This capability is expressed in 'watts' (a tribute to James Watt of the steam engine fame, denoted by the symbol W) and is a combination of volts and amps – easily calculated by multiplying them together. Watts are represented in equations by P (power). Thus:

I x V = P   (in other words amps times volts equals watts)

A WATT is a unit of power and work capability.

Electrical appliances, from simple bulbs to sophisticated electronics, are almost invariably marked with their voltage and power consumption in watts, meaning how much power the device is rated to use at that voltage. This is important information since we must know how much current a circuit will be asked to carry before the cable size is specified. It's therefore very common to see this equation transposed to yield amps – the size of the current that will flow through that circuit.

$\dfrac{P}{V}$ = I **(in other words watts divided by volts equals amps)**

Here's the calculation for, say, an electrically ravenous electric windlass:

$\dfrac{800W}{12V}$ = 66.7A (Ouch! That's a big wire we'll need)

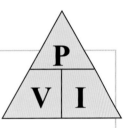

TIP: Over the years, countless electricians have relied on 'magic triangles' to nudge their memories. Simply block out the value you want and the positions of the other two will indicate what you need to do to obtain it. For example: let's say you want watts. Obscure the P at the top of the triangle and it shows that V and I must be multiplied to get the result. If in search of I, P must be divided by V, and so on.

Resistance

The last of this indispensable quartet of electrical properties has to do with 'resistance' – a term that describes any opposition to the flow of current within a circuit. Its effects were first defined in 1826 by Georg Simon Ohm whose law states:

> ***Electric current is directly proportional to voltage
> and inversely proportional to resistance.***

In less dusty language, this means that increasing voltage increases the current, while adding resistance has the opposite effect. Ohm gave his name to the unit of resistance – the ohm – the symbol of which is the Greek letter omega ( ). It is represented in equations by 'R' thus:

$I = V/R$ or $R = V/I$ or $V = I \times R$

These three equations represent Ohm's Law transposed to solve for amps, ohms, and volts in turn.

> ***An electromotive force of one volt will drive a current of one amp
> to overcome a resistance of one ohm.***

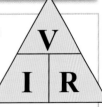

TIP: This is the second of our magic triangles. Again, simply block out the value you want and the positions of the other two will indicate what you need to do. Let's say you want volts. Obscure the V at the top of the triangle and it shows that I and R must be multiplied to get the result. If in search of I, R must be divided into V, and so on.

Sorting the symbols

It's useful to understand the distinction between the 'units' of electrical properties and their 'dimensions'.

- The symbol 'A' describes the unit of current and 'I' its dimension. Similarly:

- 'W' is the unit of power and 'P' its dimension.

- ' ' is the unit of resistance and 'R' its dimension.

- Then, just when you think you've got things sorted you discover that 'V' is the unit of electrical force and its dimension.

Power and resistance – a pause for thought

Many of us would consider a 12V system utterly safe. Grab the ends of a live wire and we can't even feel the electricity flowing through us. But if we were rash enough to do the same on a 240V domestic circuit we would know instantly we were in deep trouble – assuming we had time to think about it, that is, because we could well be dead.

But there are risks other than electrocution, and what we have learned over the previous few pages can give us an insight into where they lie.

Let's take a simple example. The incandescent lamp (commonly known as a 'bulb') in a masthead anchor light is typically 25W. On a 12V circuit it would be drawing just over 2A (see page 9 for the formula). But if the same wattage bulb were in your bedside lamp at home, plugged into a 240V socket, it would be drawing a mere 0.104A. This means that the current serving that paltry little bulb at your masthead would be about twenty times greater than its domestic equivalent.

Now we know that current is the onward march of electrons, and that the more of them that pass, the higher the amperage. Unfortunately, they don't tramp along unimpeded. Even the best conductors have some internal resistance – obstacles that get in the way of the advancing electrons, acting almost like friction.

This is sometimes unfortunate but it's not always bad news. We often harness resistance deliberately to achieve a desired effect. The filament in that light bulb, for instance, is heated to incandescence to make it burn bright.

Which demonstrates that heat is the inevitable product of current and resistance. If too large a current (amps) is asked to flow through too small a cable, the cable can seriously overheat, possibly melting the insulation and creating a short circuit or even fire. We shall be looking at the whole matter of specifying cable sizes later (see page 44), but the central message is clear:

With low voltage systems there is a significant risk of fire!

THE HYDRAULIC ANALOGY

As was mentioned at the start of this book, many of the characteristics of electricity in a circuit can be compared with those of water circulating through a plumbing system (Figure 1:6).
Useful comparisons are:

- Volts can be compared with water pressure. Electricity will only flow from a higher voltage to a lower voltage – the disparity between them being known as the 'potential difference'. Similarly, water naturally flows downhill.

- Amperes (electrical current) can be compared with the amount of water passing a given point per unit of time. Both refer to flow rate.

- Watts – the unit of power – compares to a combination of water pressure and flowrate, closely mirroring the relationship between volts and amps. In hydraulic terms a small flow of water under high pressure can have as much power as a larger flow at low pressure. The same goes for electricity.

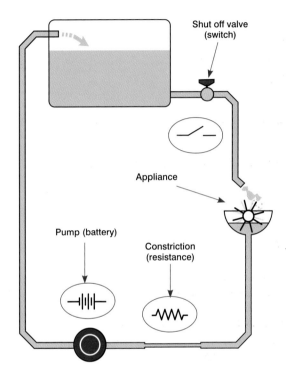

Figure 1:6 Many components in a plumbing system have their electrical equivalents – shown here with the appropriate symbols.

- High water flow rates demand big bore pipes. Similarly, large currents require cables of greater cross-sectional area.

- Both the electrical current and the water will be slowed by internal resistance and both will experience a fall-off in pressure (or voltage) due to that loss. However, the rate of flow will be the same, simply because what goes in one end of a sealed system must come out of the other.

Other comparisons could be made but, for practical purposes, our analogy has been stretched far enough. So, let's move on to the electric circuits. We can always come back if we need to.

BASIC CIRCUITS

In an electrical context the word 'circuit' means the path followed by an electric current and will include all the components it will meet on its way.

A very simple example is shown in Figure 1:7. A single lamp (the correct word for 'bulb' which refers to something you plant in your garden) is wired between the so-called positive and negative terminals of a 12V battery. The bulb, of course, brings with it some resistance – you don't get something for nothing. In exchange for the light (intense heat actually) there will be a usage of power.

Figure 1:7

Now let's assume our skipper – skilled in the ways of the sea but a couple of feet short of a fathom when it comes to electrics – decides to fit an extra reading light over his bunk. He rummages around, finds the live feed to the existing light, cuts it and wires in the new fitting.

Bedtime finds him disappointed. The lights come on all right, but they are nothing like as bright as he had hoped. What's happened to the power?

Series circuits

It's not necessary to plough through all the calculations, but it's certainly important to understand the basic principles.

Almost certainly, our man has wired in the new light as shown in Figure 1:8. This is known as a 'series' circuit, where electrical 'loads' – of whatever type and however many there may be – are strung along the wire like beads on a necklace.

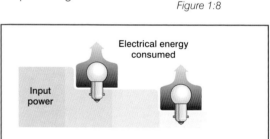

Figure 1:8

Although series circuits have their uses there are two major problems with this type of arrangement. The first is that, because each individual load presents its resistance in turn, there will be a drop in voltage after every one (Figure 1:9).

And current. Well, let's assume in our case that we have 24W lamps each offering a resistance of 6 . Applying Ohm's Law to a single lamp, we have:

$$\frac{12V}{6} = 2A$$

But in our example we have two lamps, giving 12 of resistance in total. So...

$$\frac{12V}{12} = 1A$$

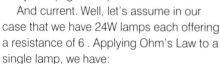

Figure 1:9

The current will be the same at any point on the circuit, but it's only half what it was before. Furthermore, the two lamps now share the voltage (6V each), meaning that the power delivered to each of them is:

6V x 1A = 6 watts of power from each of the 24W lamps we started off with.

The more loads you add, the worse the situation becomes.

A close relation to Ohm's Law is Joule's Law which defines the power dissipated by a resistor in terms of current. The equations to both can be combined, thus:

$P \text{ (watts)} = I^2 \cdot R$

If you apply this equation to the calculations opposite, you will find the results agree.

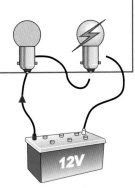

The second problem with series circuits is that if any of the loads fail, the continuity of the circuit would be broken and the whole circuit will go down (Figure 1:10). If one of the lamps in our example was to blow, then the power to the other would be interrupted and so it, too, would be dark.

There has to be a better way. And there is!

Figure 1:10

Parallel circuits

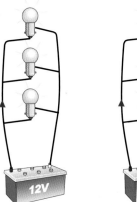
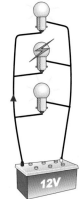

Figure: 1:11

Figure 1:11 shows an arrangement where the loads (lamps) are wired like rungs on a ladder between electrical cables (one positive, the other negative) led to a power source – in this case a battery. These loads are said to be wired 'in parallel' and this is by far the most common type of circuit found afloat. With good reason.

The first advantage is that no single load failure can cause the whole circuit to fail, since all of the other loads continue to be connected to the battery. Indeed, in our example, even if two lamps blew out, the third would remain lit.

What could be less obvious are the effects on voltages and currents, for these go against intuition. To see what's going on, it may help to redraw Figure 1:11 as a simple circuit diagram, substituting conventional resistor symbols for the lamps.

In a series circuit the total resistances is the sum of all of them – for example $5 + 5 + 10 = 20$ (Figure 1:12). But this isn't true of parallel circuits. The reason for this is that each resistor provides another path for the current and the overall resistance therefore reduces. In fact:

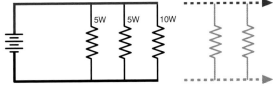

Figure: 1:12

"The sum of the reciprocals of all the resistors is equal to the reciprocal of the total circuit resistance."

That's quite a mouthful, but its significance can be explained by example. If all the parallel resistors are the same you can find their combined resistance by dividing the resistance of just one of them by how many resistors there are. For instance, if you had three 18 resistors in parallel their effect would be the equivalent of a single 6 – e.g. 18/3.

It's a little more complicated if the resistors are different. Now we must take the reciprocals of each of them (by dividing 1 by their values), add them together and you have the reciprocal of their combined resistance.

$$1/R_1 + 1/R_2 + 1/R_3 = 1/R_{(total)}$$

For the resistors in our earlier series example this would be:

$$1/5 + 1/5 + 1/10 = 5/10, \text{ and the reciprocal of this is 2}$$

The total current for a 12V circuit can then be determined using:

$$I = V/R \dots \text{ so } 12/2 = 6A$$

Finally, I=V/R will give us the current flowing through each individual resistor:

$$12/5 = 2.4A$$
$$12/5 = 2.4A$$
$$12/10 = 1.2A$$

Which all adds up to the 6A we know to be the total current.

MEET THE MULTIMETER

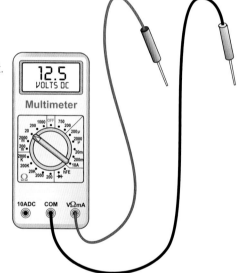

The most important – let's be frank, indispensable – diagnostic device to have in your electrical toolbox is a multimeter. These come in various types – the older style analogue meters with a pivoting needle, and the increasingly popular digital type where the various readings are displayed on an LCD panel. With their delicate mechanisms, analogue meters are quite fragile, leaving the digital variety the clear winner for a life at sea. From hereon in this book it will be this type we refer to.

Functions vary from model to model but should be capable of measuring DC volts, amperes and ohms. Some meters also include a feature for testing electrical continuity, with a beep confirming that a circuit is unbroken. Many multimeters require that the probe be reconnected to another terminal when changing from current to voltage mode. Read your meter's instructions for full details.

With inexpensive meters you must manually select each operating range – e.g. the bracket in which you expect a value to fall – but more expensive instruments are 'autoranging', meaning they will choose the appropriate range for themselves.

CAUTION: Always be very careful connecting a multimeter to a mains supply. If in any doubt, call in an expert.

Measuring amps

Set the multimeter to register amps. The meter must become part of the circuit to measure current, and you can often make this connection across the terminals of an open switch as shown in Figure 1:13. If this isn't possible, break the circuit at some other convenient point. In this mode the meter offers very little resistance so as not to impose its own effects on the circuit, thereby distorting the readings.

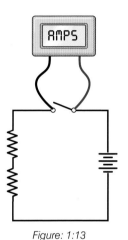

Figure: 1:13

Measuring volts

By contrast, in voltmeter mode the meter's internal resistance is very high, discouraging the current from flowing through it. The circuit is left intact – that's to say, unbroken – and voltage or voltage drop can then be determined by measuring across any components within it. See Figure 1:14.

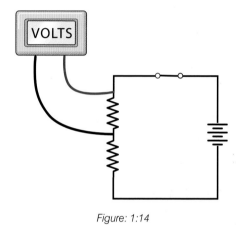

Figure: 1:14

Measuring resistance

Any existing power supply must be disabled before you start. Then a battery inside the meter introduces its own small current, measures the voltage produced, and calculates the resistance from that. Whole circuits can be measured as shown in Figure 1:15 but individual components must first be disconnected from the circuit.

Incidentally, at room temperature the resistance of a light bulb (lamp) is a mere fraction of what it is when incandescent. Nothing meaningful can be gained by measuring it. Rely on its specified power rating instead.

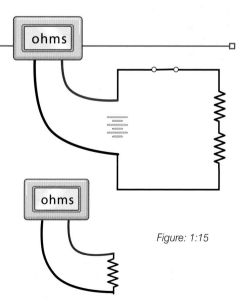

Figure: 1:15

CHAPTER 2

BATTERIES

The word 'battery' should rightly mean a grouping of similar objects – cannons being an obvious military example. However, in the electrical context it has come to describe any 'cell' that can produce or store electricity, whether single or arranged in a group.

Electrical cells can be divided into two separate camps – those that can be recharged and those that can't. Those that can't are known as 'primary cells' and depend upon chemical processes that become irreversibly exhausted once the active ingredients are spent. In practical terms this means that we use these 'batteries' until they are dead, then throw them away – hopefully with care, since some of their constituents are toxic.

Extremely useful though primary cells are – powering torches, portable radios and the like – of more importance to seafarers are the rechargeable batteries that 'store' the electricity we use to power our onboard systems. These are made up of 'secondary cells' connected in series. Of course, secondary cells don't actually store anything. What they do is convert electrical energy into a form of chemical energy that can be released whenever we need it to provide a current. And they can do it over and over again.

So, how?

WET LEAD-ACID BATTERIES

It isn't essential to know how batteries work, but it helps. Originally invented by Frenchman Gaston Planté in 1859, lead acid batteries have been with us for a long time. And although the technology has been refined over the years, the principles remain much the same.

The 12V batteries that power the majority of boats consist of six 2.1V cells wired in series. The main components of each cell are astonishingly simple: just a pair of 'electrode' plates immersed in an 'electrolyte' of sulphuric acid (H_2SO_4) and distilled water. Sulphuric acid – a compound of hydrogen, sulphur and oxygen – is a very reactive substance that willingly disassociates into hydrogen ions and sulphate groups. Combined with water it becomes conductive.

The so-called 'negative' plate is made up of lead (Pb), and the 'positive' plate of lead dioxide (PbO_2). If we connect a resistive load between the two terminals the battery begins to discharge and a number of chemical reactions are triggered – the product of which is an electric current.

During the discharge cycle (Figure 2:1) both plates will be converted into lead sulphate ($PbSO_4$). The sulphuric acid will throw itself enthusiastically into the formation of other compounds and the electrolyte will become almost entirely water.

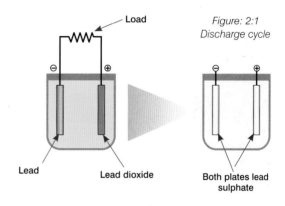

Figure: 2:1
Discharge cycle

Lead · Lead dioxide · Both plates lead sulphate

Happily for us, the situation is reversible. By applying an external reverse electric current to the cell it can be restored to its former state. The plates will be returned to lead and lead dioxide respectively and the sulphuric acid will be recovered from its temporary lodgings and reassembled into its original form. In short, the battery will have been recharged (Figure 2:2).

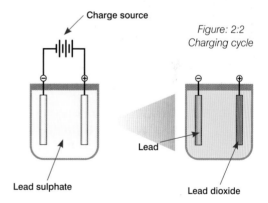

Figure: 2:2
Charging cycle

Charge source · Lead sulphate · Lead · Lead dioxide

Thus, the discharge reaction will be:

Anode: $Pb + HSO_4^-$ becomes $PbSO_4 \, H^+ \, 2e^-$

Cathode: $PbO_2 + HSO_4^- + 3H^+ + 2e^-$ becomes $PbSO_4 + 2H_2O$

CAUTION: Hydrogen and oxygen gas will be given off during charging – particularly if the charge process is too vigorous. Since this is a potentially explosive mixture, wet lead-acid battery compartments must be well ventilated.

An ion is an atom or molecule that has lost or gained at least one electron, leaving it positively or negatively charged. Way back on page 6 we learned that an electrically neutral atom has the same number of protons (positive) as electrons (negative). It follows that if it were to lose one or more electrons, the protons would dominate and it would become a positively charged ion. If, however, it were to gain electrons, these would be dominant and would make it a negatively charged ion.

Ions are identified in the same manner as their electrically neutral parents but with a superscript indicating how many electrons (if more than one) the atom has lost or gained and whether it is positively or negatively charged.

For example H^+ tells us this is a positive hydrogen ion with – confusingly – one less electron. SO_4^- is a sulphate with two extra electrons and has a net negative charge.

BATTERY CONSTRUCTION

Planté's prototype battery used thin lead plates and – remarkable though it was – its capacity was pretty modest. One reason was because only the surfaces of the active material were in contact with the electrolyte. To overcome this problem, some modern battery plates consist of rigid grids filled with the active materials formulated into porous pastes that can be readily penetrated by the electrolyte. With the whole thickness of each plate now flooded, the contact area increases hugely, as does the battery's capacity.

Also, whereas Planté's battery had just a pair of plates per cell, each cell of a modern battery contains several, interleaved so closely that they rely on insulated 'separators' to prevent them touching (see Figure 2:3). It's the nature of these plates that determines what sort of battery it is.

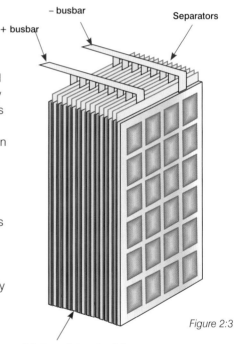

– busbar

+ busbar

Separators

Interleaved + and – plates

Figure 2:3

Cold cranking amps (CCA)

This shouldn't concern many boat owners but it's worth mentioning in passing. In cold climates, engines become more difficult to start at a time when batteries are less efficient. A battery's CCA refers to the number of amps it can support for 30 seconds at -18°C (0°F) before it's discharged to unusable levels. The higher the CCA number the better.

Automotive batteries

These are almost certainly the type we are most familiar with. We turn a key, the starter motor cranks over and our car bursts into life. Now, starter motors are muscular beasts. And hungry. They need a lot of current and need it fast – but only for a few seconds before they are recharged by the engine's alternator.

Automotive batteries are designed specifically for the job. Each cell contains a large number of very thin plates, presenting the maximum amount of surface area to the electrolyte. This enables them to release large currents extremely quickly – exactly what the starter motor (and the motorist) wants.

But there's a price to pay for this, for these are the sprinters of the battery world – fast in short bursts but hopeless over longer distances. If deeply discharged – say by the sustained loads demanded of a boat's domestic system – their fragile plates will soon buckle, the active material will be dislodged from their grids and fall to the bottom of the casing where it will short-circuit the plates. The battery will be dead. Permanently.

Automotive type batteries have no place on a boat, other than perhaps to start engines. And even that is debatable.

Deep cycle batteries

If car batteries are sprinters then these are the marathon runners. They are sometimes called 'traction' batteries because they are often used on forklifts, golf carts, invalid chairs and the like – all of which need electrical power to be delivered hour after hour. The term 'deep cycle' means to discharge a battery to a level well below its fully charged state. But that doesn't mean dead flat. All batteries suffer every time they are cycled – some much more than others. For example, to repeatedly discharge a starter type battery to 50% would destroy it after only a few dozen cycles. On the other hand a dedicated deep cycle battery might withstand 1000 or more cycles before it met the same fate, and perhaps twice that number if only allowed to discharge to 20%.

The main reason that deep cycle batteries survive longer is simple: their plates are structurally more rugged. They are usually of thicker, solid lead – rather than paste – and there are fewer of them (Figure 2:4). The downside of this arrangement is that the plates release the current relatively slowly so this type are less able to deliver lots of current in a hurry. This makes them hopeless for engine starting.

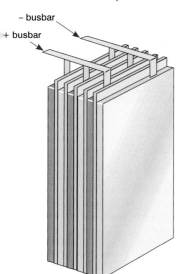

– busbar
+ busbar

Figure 2:4

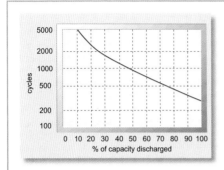

The deeper you discharge any battery, the shorter it will survive. This graph shows a typical deep cycle battery regularly cycled to increasing depths. The effects on service life are clear.

Go easy on your batteries and they will serve you for much longer.

CAUTION: When it comes to deep cycling, beware of optimistic claims. If possible, check the manufacturers' specifications before choosing.

'Leisure' type batteries

These are the middle-distance runners – a compromise between starting and deep cycle batteries and popular on boats which only carry a single battery or where the electrical demands are modest. They are punchy enough to start smaller engines and can withstand some deep cycling but they perform neither role as satisfactorily as the specialised types and will not have the long service life of true deep cyclers.

Sealed lead-acid (SLA) batteries

All of the preceding batteries have liquid electrolyte sloshing about inside vented containers. Not a great idea on boats which, to put it mildly, tend to get tossed around a bit. It's one thing to break some crockery in a knockdown – quite another to let sulphuric acid loose in your bilges. So, to have sealed batteries has obvious merits.

The word 'sealed' needs qualification. All lead-acid batteries generate gaseous hydrogen and oxygen when charging – much of which is reabsorbed in the more sophisticated types. However, if overcharged even the best of them can suffer build-ups of pressure which must be released through special safety valves before they burst. This is a one-way process. Gases can escape, nothing can get in. So far as their internal workings are concerned, such batteries are maintenance free.

Gel cell batteries

These have been around for over thirty years and are deservedly popular. The feature that distinguishes them from wet lead-acid batteries is that the liquid electrolyte has been converted into a gel by adding colloidal silica (silicon dioxide). The combination of a sealed casing and a viscous electrolyte adds up to an effectively spill-proof battery.

Gel cells can be used for starting smaller engines but they are better suited to the somewhat more tranquil role of supporting domestic services. Treated properly, they can be very long-lived, but they do need special charging regimes to keep them in good shape.

Absorbed Glass Mat (AGM) batteries

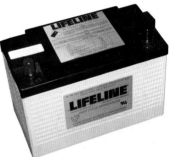

So far as construction is concerned, the name says it all. This most recent of all lead-acid technologies was first developed for the none-but-the-best spheres of aviation and the military. Inside you would find that the battery plates are interleaved with fine-stranded glass mats that hold the electrolyte in place by capillary action.

AGM batteries have very low internal resistance. This makes them super fast when it comes to both accepting and delivering current. In other words, they can be charged very rapidly and will also deliver the quick punch of power needed to turn over engines.

An interesting variation on the AGM theme is the spiral cell Optima type, whose shape resembles a six-pack of toilet rolls – a clue to what's going on inside. Instead of racking the plates in the conventional side by side manner, the Optima rolls them together like a swiss roll with the glass mats into cylinders before sealing them into their characteristic enclosures.

AGMs aren't cheap so it's worth looking after them. Charging is such an important subject that it deserves – and gets – its own chapter in this book. So, much more on this starting on page 28....

CAUTION: When it comes to comparing batteries there's a lot of conflicting information about. The wise skipper will check each manufacturer's data to ensure they are getting exactly what they want. And more expensive doesn't always mean better value for every application. A long distance sailor would benefit from top-of-the-line batteries, whereas a weekender might get along nicely with the budget variety.

Battery capacity

The most important attribute for any service battery is its capacity – that's to say, how much use we can get out of it. The unit that commonly defines this is the 'amp-hour' (Ah) – the number of amps we could expect from a battery assuming it was discharged over a period of time. For the purpose of describing capacity this is usually 20 hours (often called C/20) for most manufacturers, though 10 hours (C/10) was once common in Britain.

That 'period of time' bit is important. A 200Ah battery discharged at 10A per hour will be dead flat (10.5V) after 20 hours. You might conclude from this that if you discharged that same battery at a rate of 20A per hour it would last for 10 hours – i.e. 200/20 = 10. Unfortunately, you would be disappointed. The faster a battery is discharged, the fewer amp-hours it will yield. These effects were first approximated by a gent called Peukert back in 1897, giving rise to the equation:

Capacity = I^nT

Where 'n' is the Peukert number (or exponent) and 'T' the time in hours.

But please don't reach for your calculator. This equation should have a prominent warning sign hung around its neck since it's often misused – usually by transposing it (to $T = C/I^n$) in an attempt to predict how long a battery will last when discharged at a certain rate. To apply it to our 200Ah (C/20) battery, or similar, would result in nonsensical answers – not because the equation is flawed but because it's not being used in its original context.

The proper equation to use is shown below along with a graph illustrating the influence of the Peukert effect. Note that it isn't all bad news. There's another side to the coin: namely, that a slower discharge than its C/20 rate will increase a battery's capacity. For instance, if the discharge amperage on our 200Ah was reduced to a measly 1A, its capacity would swell to a lusty 399Ah – virtually double!

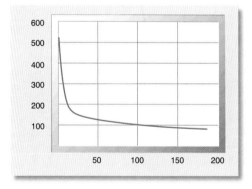

$$T = \frac{C}{(C/R)^n} \times \frac{R}{C}$$

Where:
T = time (hours)
C = Capacity (Ah)
I = Discharge current
n = Peukert exponent
R = Hour rating (ie C/20)

Good quality gel or AGM batteries might have Peukert numbers around the 1.1 mark while standard flooded types could be 1.3 and upwards. The cheapest batteries might hit a dismal 1.8.

Battery monitoring

Of course, to repeatedly cycle a 12V battery down to 10.5V would soon see it on the scrap heap. If we want to get good value from our batteries we should consider 11.7V to be the absolute limit – i.e. dead flat. But even this is undesirable, still putting the battery under unnecessary stress and hastening its slide into decrepitude. Over the years a fair amount of experience has been gained and it's generally agreed that to discharge to 50% (of full charge) to 12.2V is a sensible trade-off between usefulness and battery life, though to set the limit to 75% of full charge (12.4V) would be even better.

Which means we need to keep an eye on the charge state of our batteries.

Hydrometer

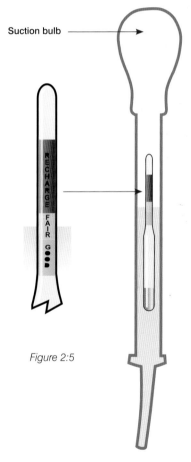

Suction bulb

The first method takes advantage of the changing Specific Gravity (SG) of the electrolyte. Sulphuric acid has an SG of 1.83, meaning it's 1.83 times heavier than water (SG 1.0). When the two are combined to form the electrolyte, the SG strikes a compromise somewhere around the 1.27 mark. As a battery discharges, the sulphuric acid is progressively taken up by the chemical changes, while the water content of the electrolyte increases. By measuring the SG at any point in the cycle you can therefore closely approximate the battery's state of charge at that time.

In practice, a small quantity of electrolyte from each cell in turn is sucked into a bulbed syringe containing a tiny calibrated float. The level at which this floats indicates the SG (Figure 2:5).

Battery state of charge		
% of full charge	**12V DC**	**Specific Gravity**
100%	12.7	1.265 – 1.275
75%	12.4	1.225 – 1.235
50%	12.2	1.190 – 1.200
25%	12.0	1.155 – 1.165
0%	<11.7	1.120 – 1.130

Figure 2:5

CAUTION: As we saw on Page 17 both plates on a severely flat battery become lead sulphate. If allowed to stay that way the sulphate will harden and the battery will be ruined. ALWAYS KEEP YOUR BATTERIES AS FULLY CHARGED AS POSSIBLE. (See battery maintenance on Page 69)

Continuous monitoring

The simplest device is the humble voltmeter (Figure 2:6) – preferably with an expanded scale spanning the small range of voltage significant to lead-acid batteries. But these are rapidly being shouldered aside by electronic instruments of far greater versatility and usefulness.

Specifications and functions vary from brand to brand, but a typical battery monitor will show:

Figure 2:6

- A multicolour light bar (Figure 2:7) of some sort giving you the state of charge at a glance.

- System voltage

- System current

- Percentage of capacity remaining

- Amp hours consumed or gained

- Time before recharging is required at current consumption rate

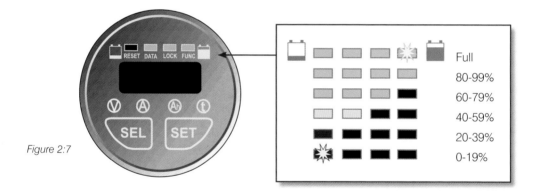

Figure 2:7

Both battery capacity and Peukert exponents must be entered manually for prediction functions to work, and if these are in error then it's possible for the monitor to get out of sync – perhaps indicating that the battery is running out of capacity when actually it's in good shape. Most monitors have a simple synchronising procedure that will soon put things in order. The precise details should be found in its manual!

We haven't finished with batteries entirely because they feature strongly in Chapter 4. Care and maintenance is covered in Chapter 10.

CAUTION: All batteries deteriorate with time, losing performance as they age. Although their external appearance might look the same, they will never be the same as they were when new. Allowances must be made.

CHAPTER 3

THE ENGINE AND ITS BASIC CIRCUITS

Circuit diagrams can be daunting – a maze of lines whose function often bewilders. And there is no respite in sight. As our boats become more electrically dependant, so do their circuits. Viewed as a whole, they can be almost unfathomable. But not if we take them step by step, section by section. So, let's kick off with the primary engine circuit.

The days of hand-cranked engines are over. A few older designs might retain the feature but the trend is irrevocably towards electrical starting. A key is turned or a button pressed, and the beast springs into life. A typical starting circuit is shown in Figure 3:1 and the sequence goes as follows:

- The battery isolator disables the whole circuit so must first be switched on to provide a power source.

- The first turn of the ignition key takes it to the 'On' position. This powers up the various gauges and engine warning sensors (of which more soon). On most systems the oil pressure alarm will sound and the low/no charging light will come on.

- The second turn of the key brings us to the 'Start' position. This energises the coil in the starter motor solenoid, thus closing internal contacts. This allows a heavy current from the starter battery to turn the motor and crank the engine. The ignition key is spring-loaded and returns itself to the 'On' position. Simple push-button switches are sometimes used to perform the same task.

- As the revs pick up, the charging light should go out and the audible oil pressure alarm mercifully stop.

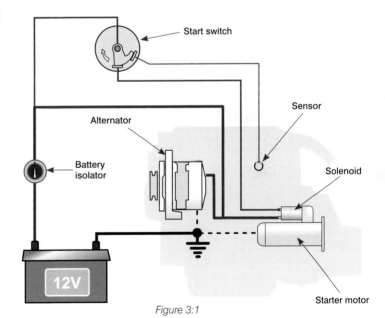

Figure 3:1

TIP: For no more than the price of a good takeaway meal you can buy a 'workshop' manual for your engine. Amongst the other useful information will be a detailed circuit diagram for your engine.

Engine stop

Once started, most diesel engines will run without electricity (common rail type and electronically controlled engines won't). To turn them off requires operation of a small stop lever on the injection pump. Many smaller and older engines use a mechanical pull cable to achieve this – an admirably simple arrangement – but the trend is inexorably towards electrical control.

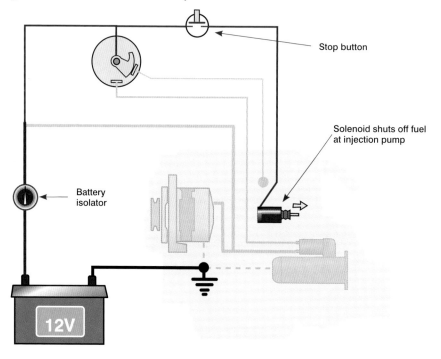

Figure 3:2 Engine stop – electric solenoid type

Engines whose roots come from an automotive background can often be stopped simply by turning off the 'ignition' key, rather as you might in your car. This breaks the circuit to a solenoid control valve that allows the engine to run. Deprived of power, the solenoid relaxes and the engine stops.

The stop control on dedicated marine engines usually does exactly the opposite. The solenoid is inactive while the engine runs but, when the moment comes, is energised to pull the stop lever to shut it down. With this system you will either find a stop button on the control panel or must turn the key deliberately (and usually anticlockwise) to an OFF position.

Which seems like a good time to talk about sensors and senders.

SENSORS AND SENDERS

These transducers are the reconnaissance scouts that warn of impending problems for your engine. The difference between them is that sensors provide the data for instruments monitoring the rise and fall of various properties while senders simply trigger alarms. Some multi-functional transducers will do both.

Their number and complexity depends on the sophistication of your system, but the minimum will be:

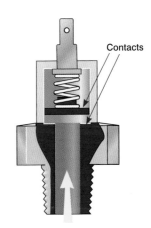
Contacts

- **Lubricating oil pressure. If the alarm sounds it could mean either that the oil level is very low – perhaps a leak or simply burned away – or that the crankshaft bearings are on their last legs.**

Figure 3:3 Oil pressure sensors open and break the circuit as pressure builds. This silences the alarm.

- **Cooling water temperature. If you hear this alarm it could be that the engine's thermostat has failed or that the raw water supply has become blocked.**

- **Low or no charge from the alternator. Either a serious system fault or the alternator's drive belt has broken. The latter could also be the cause of the rise in water temperature.**

Not exactly essential but certainly useful are:

Exhaust overheat alarm.
This provides a valuable early warning of an overheating engine, most importantly before super-hot gases get a chance to destroy those parts of your exhaust which are not heat-resistant. Also, because water temperature alarms only work when immersed, a catastrophic loss of the fresh water coolant will render them useless.

Excessively hot gases are sensed by a probe piercing the exhaust hose, sounding the audible alarm, left.

On the other hand, exhaust alarms signal any problems within seconds.

Tachometer or rev counter – often incorporating an engine hour meter. Most tachos depend either on sensing a pulse from the alternator's windings or by counting the transits of a small magnet attached to the engine's flywheel. A third method – perhaps of interest to anyone wanting an easily installed retro-fit – uses a small transducer clamped to the high-pressure feed between the injection pump and an injector. The instrument shown left is of this type.

CHAPTER 4

ENGINE CHARGING AND BATTERY MANAGEMENT

When two or more batteries are connected so they can operate as one they become a 'bank', mimicking their monetary counterparts except that there are no helpful overdrafts where batteries are concerned. You can only take out what's already been put in and no more.

But before we move on and discuss the various ways batteries are grouped together and controlled, we need to think about where those inputs come from. For smaller to mid-size boats – i.e. those unlikely to have a dedicated engine powered generator – the principal sources are from a charger connected to shore power, when alongside, and the engine alternator, when in service. Other options are explored in the next chapter.

ALTERNATORS

These energetic little machines are actually based on a very uncomplicated concept. Figure 4:1 shows a rudimentary alternator. A strong magnet is rotated between the jaws of an iron yoke. The variations in the magnetic field produces an electric current that flows in different directions depending upon the rotational position of the magnet. If viewed on an oscilloscope it would be seen as a 'sine curve' – the characteristic shape of an 'alternating' current (AC) from which, of course, the alternator gets its name.

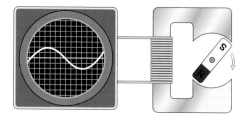

Figure 4:1

Figure 4:2 shows a rather more refined model – still a long way short of a practical alternator but in principle very close to the real thing. This time the rotor is an electromagnet, energised by the 'field coil' which draws its power from outside via 'slip ring' contacts. The rotor passes across the faces of three equally spaced 'stator' coils, generating an AC current in each of them in turn. Because there's a time difference between each pass, the three outputs emerge 120° out of phase, combining to make what's known with breathtaking aptness as a 'three phase current'.

Single phase alternators do exist but you can see from Figure 4:3 that the output would be very lumpy with brutal peaks and troughs. From now on let's assume we're talking about 3-phase units which produce much smoother currents.

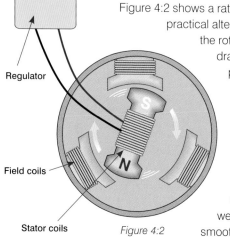

Regulator

Field coils

Stator coils

Figure 4:2

AC to DC

To convert the initial AC harvest from our stator coils to the direct currents (DC) needed to charge our batteries calls for the services of a 'rectifier' – almost invariably built into the alternator. Rectifiers rely on 'diodes' which you can think of as electrical one-way valves – that's to say they allow the current to flow only in one direction.

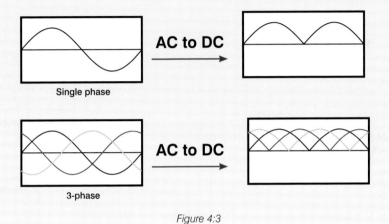

Figure 4:3

RECTIFIERS

The most common rectifiers have six diodes arranged as shown here. As the polarity in each stator coil's waveform changes, the currents discover there's only one way for them through the maze of diodes. This brings them out at the exit with their polarities all the same – our DC supply. On most alternators, the diodes are clearly visible on the back.

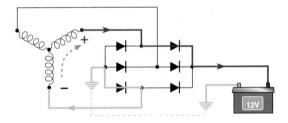

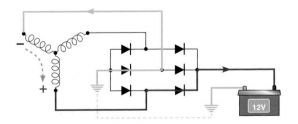

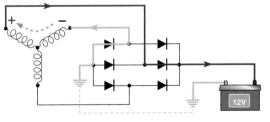

Solve the diode maze! The current from each coil can only find one way out.

THE REGULATOR

The output from an alternator depends on three things:

- **The number of turns in the stator coils**
- **The rotational speed**
- **The magnetic strength of the rotor**

Obviously, we can have no influence on the specification of the coils since this is down to the manufacturer. Neither would we want to be forever altering the throttle setting just to please the alternator. This leaves varying the rotor's magnetism as the only remaining option. And that's exactly what the voltage regulator does on our behalf.

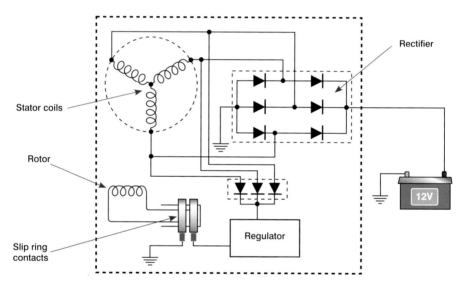

Figure 4:4

In order to function, the regulator has to have input information to act on, and this can take two forms: 'machine sensing' or 'battery sensing' – both phrases being pretty much self-explanatory. The first describes an alternator that monitors its own output, while the second type senses the voltage of the battery under charge. One physical distinction between the two types is that battery sensed alternators have an extra terminal – four instead of three – to connect the sensing lead to the battery.

The regulator works by increasing or decreasing the power to the field windings and can be connected to the positive or negative side, thereby gaining the logical description P-type or N-type to distinguish between the two. P-type tends to be favoured in the USA with N-type generally being preferred in Europe. For most purposes the difference to us is unimportant.

As with the rectifiers, most 'standard' regulators are incorporated into the alternator. They are sealed units whose internal workings are best left hidden. We shall be meeting the considerably more sophisticated 'smart charging' types soon.

Bad deals for diodes

Most battery isolation switches bear some sort of label imploring us to make sure the engine is stopped before the power is switched off. This is good advice since not to do so can destroy an alternator's diodes at a stroke.

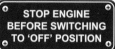

STOP ENGINE BEFORE SWITCHING TO 'OFF' POSITION

   The cause of this mischief is easily explained. By prematurely switching off you will have open-circuited the connection between battery and alternator, thereby slamming the door on any charging current. The resulting voltage spike will overwhelm those tender little diodes, reducing them to molten blobs in an instant. This is probably the most common cause of alternator failure.

   Another possible threat can occur by turning off the ignition switch on diesels with manually operated stop controls. This doesn't open-circuit the battery connections but it does disrupt the regulator's control over the field windings, meaning the output voltage could build unchecked.

Better deals for diodes

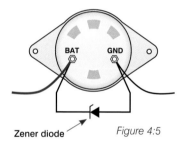

Zener diode   *Figure 4:5*

Fortunately, we can guard against our own carelessness by fitting inexpensive devices known variously as 'transient spike protectors', 'surge protectors' or, less stuffily, 'snubbers' – all describing the same thing. These employ Zener diodes (after American physicist Clarence Zener) which, under most circumstances, have the same one-way properties of ordinary diodes but will allow current to flow in the reverse direction should it exceed a certain voltage. Connected between the alternator's output and ground (Figure 4:5), a Zener diode forms a sort of electrical safety valve that de-energises the field coils by dumping excessive output to ground. This kills the output, thereby sparing the other diodes. Snubbers should be as close to the alternator as possible – often most conveniently between the BAT (for battery, often simply B) and the GND (ground) terminals of the alternator itself.

Improving output

Whereas the engine hours clocked up by power vessels might be more than enough to keep their batteries topped up, the same can't be said for sailboats which tend to spend much less time motoring. Faced with shorter periods of engine charging, it's not surprising that sailing skippers contrive to wring as much as possible from what limited periods they have.

   A typical marine alternator with an inbuilt regulator springs from the automotive industry. In its shore-bound role this charging combination is intended to serve in situations where the engine runs more or less continuously – first replacing the electrical power spent cranking the engine, then supporting the ongoing systems such as lights, fans, wipers, radios etc – demands not unlike those on powerboats.

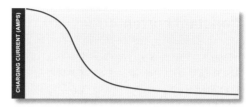

The regulators adopt a principle known as 'taper charging' where the output voltage is preset to somewhere between 14.0V and 14.4V and the current is determined by whatever the battery will accept at any time. Figure 4:6 shows both the simplicity and limitations of this approach.

Figure 4:6

A partially discharged battery at first offers little resistance to the alternator output, which pours in pretty much unopposed. Soon, however, the chemical changes wrought by the charging process cause the battery's internal resistance to rise. Now facing something of a headwind, the current drops and the battery is being no more than trickle charged. Eventually, the alternator's output voltage is matched by that of the battery and that's game over for now.

This might seem fine but there's a snag. A lead acid battery won't be hurried. It balks at such an uncouth approach and will probably have reached only about 80% of its charge capacity. Teasing and seducing a battery to accept as much charge as possible calls for more subtlety than taper charge regulators can muster.

External control regulators such as this are intended to make the most of your alternator and batteries

Smart regulators

This is an area constantly subject to development and where the claims of the various manufacturers often conflict – occasionally in shrill tones. However, for the cruising sailor there are significant benefits in boosting an alternator's efficiency by managing its output more intelligently than the standard taper charge arrangement permits.

But be warned. Over-ambitious charge regimes can damage batteries – particularly sealed types where electrolyte losses can never be replaced. It's very important to ensure that whatever regulator you use will not cause undue harm. The most advanced units can be programmed to deal with specific battery types: unsealed lead acid, deep cycle lead acid, sealed gel, and AGM being representative. Some also monitor battery and alternator temperatures, adjusting the charging curves accordingly whilst ensuring that nothing is going amiss.

All smart regulators convert machine sensing alternators (the most common – see page 30) to battery sensing (much the better option). They are almost invariably bulkhead mounted, with connecting wires running to the alternators and batteries they serve. They divide into two distinct groups:

Constant current regulation

These work in conjunction with the inbuilt regulator and are often called 'boosters' – though in some instances this word doesn't do them justice since the most advanced will also work as standalone units.

When working in tandem – by far the commonest arrangement – failure of the external controller simply passes the reins back to the original regulator. Understandably, many skippers find this back-up facility reassuring.

Their precise functions vary from unit to unit, with the simplest usually being the least expensive. Overall this type tends to occupy the economy end of the market, but they are still capable of giving valuable service in all but the most demanding circumstances.

Multi-step charging

Top of the line regulators can control the charging regimes even more subtly, thus squeezing the last drop of potential battery charging capacity out of the process. Again, not all units perform in exactly the same way but the following sequence is typical:

■ STEP 1: Charging is delayed for a short time to allow the engine to warm up.

■ STEP 2: The regulator ramps up the voltage slowly, thus avoiding any sudden loads on the alternator belt.

■ STEP 3: Bulk charge – the most aggressive stage. This will charge the battery to about 80% capacity in the shortest possible time.

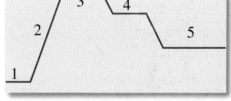

Figure 4:7

■ STEP 4: The regulator ramps down to the 'absorption charge', allowing the battery to accept yet more charge – i.e. to reach as near 100% as possible. This has the additional benefit of reconditioning the battery.

■ STEP 5: With the battery fully replenished, the regulator sets about maintaining a 'float charge' to keep the battery topped up whilst satisfying any ongoing loads that could drain it. Over an extended period, it will then alternate between absorption and float charges.

> **!** **WARNING!** Most regulators from the US are intended for P type alternators, with N type being more common on engines sold in Europe. So check for compatibility. Some manufacturers supply both types. If not, alternators can be converted from one type to another – a relatively simple task but one best left to the professionals.

BATTERY CHARGING SYSTEMS

In the most basic DC systems the alternator charges a single battery which, in turn, supplies the various electrical demands. Clearly there are limitations and risks with such an arrangement. Should the battery become deeply discharged it might become incapable of restarting the engine – not a big problem if you can hand crank it but crippling if you can't – particularly since there may now not be enough power left to summon help by radio.

Not surprisingly, only very small craft are likely to have such crude systems. By far the majority have at least two batteries and some means of managing both their charging and use.

Manual switching

There are various ways of achieving full personal control of how batteries are charged and discharged, but the most common is by way of '1, 2, Both or Off' switches. These allow a skipper to choose:

■ **Either battery (or bank) to be charged or used singly, or…**

■ **… connected together as a single battery bank.**

There are many thousands of older boats afloat with this type of circuit and some claim this is the best method. By conserving one battery you will always have enough power to start the engine. But note that phrase 'personal control'. The responsibility for battery management rests entirely in human hands and there are various pitfalls to trap the unwary:

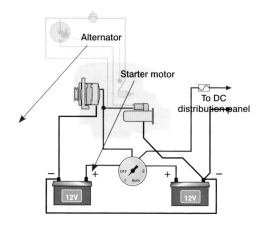

Battery selector
and isolator

Figure 4:8

■ **Unless carefully managed, there's a risk that the batteries will never reach full charge. They will deteriorate faster as a result.**

■ **Switching to the 'Off' position with the engine running will destroy the alternator diodes (see p31).**

■ **Using the batteries in the 'Both' position – and some skippers do as a matter of course – connects them in parallel. This is fine when charging but, if you forget to isolate one battery when under load, you incur the same risk as with a single battery system – namely depleting them both below useful limits.**

■ **If you have one full battery and one severely depleted, switching to 'Both' will see one drain into the other – possibly rendering both of them useless.**

Automatic split charging

Charging circuits incorporating 'battery isolators' or 'splitting diodes' are very popular on British boats. The charging current divides at the isolator, with the greater share going to whichever battery needs the most – that's to say offers the greater potential difference. In their roles as 'one-way valves' the diodes then prevent either battery discharging into the other – though there's usually a switch to cross connect them deliberately in emergencies. Output to the distribution panel is manually controlled via a switch.

There's a robust simplicity about such systems, but they also come with problems. Namely:

■ There is a voltage drop across the diodes of about 0.7 – 1 volt. This is not a problem for a battery sensed alternator (see p30) which will be aware of the drop and boost the voltage accordingly. But a machine sensed alternator – unfortunately, the type fitted as standard on many engines – will be oblivious of any loss and, therefore, won't deliver the correct voltage to the batteries. It's possible to fool the regulator with a bit of internal surgery to the alternator but the easiest solution is to fit an external controller which instantly converts the system to battery sensing (see p32).

■ Figure 4:9 shows a typical installation, having a dedicated engine start battery and a couple of domestic batteries connected in parallel to form a bank. Unlike starter batteries which may never experience deep cycling, domestic banks regularly take a hammering. The upshot of this injustice can result in frequent disparities in charge levels between the two sets. In the electrical stampede to top up the domestic bank, it's quite possible to overcharge – and damage – the starter battery.

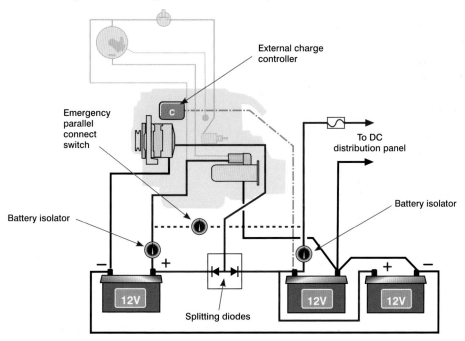

Figure 4:9

Battery combiners

First developed in the USA these devices are gaining popularity worldwide. The main advantage they bring is that, unlike diodes, they cause no voltage drop. This means that machine sensed alternators will work unimpaired, without modification or the necessity for external charge controllers.

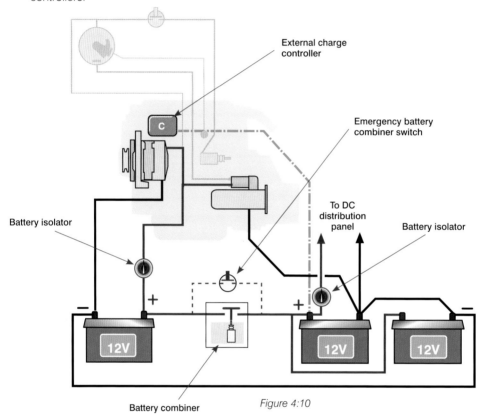

Figure 4:10

Battery combiners are heavy duty, voltage sensitive relays (VSRs). With the engine at rest the VSR is open and the starter and domestic batteries are isolated from each other. Once the engine starts, the VSR monitors the starter battery voltage, waits until it reaches full charge (usually 13.7V) then closes the circuit allowing the charge current to reach the other bank. When the engine stops, the voltage falls, the VSR opens the circuit, and the two sets are isolated once more. This arrangement prevents the starter battery from being inadvertently discharged.

The most advanced combiners will monitor up to three battery banks simultaneously, managing your charging for you and protecting against harmful overcharging. This can be useful if you have other sources of power. If, say, a wind generator (see page 39) brought your domestic bank up to full charge, the combiner would direct the surplus power to any other battery that might need it.

Apart from hard cash, a further price you pay is associated with all complex devices – a somewhat greater risk of component failure.

BIGGER IS BETTER

There's a triangular relationship between generation, storage and consumption – and a well designed installation will balance those three considerations to make sure that the first two will satisfy the third.

The conventional approach is to deal with that third issue first. This involves conducting a detailed audit of your electrical consumption by listing all of the onboard appliances, estimating their daily usage in hours – both at sea and at anchor – and totting up the total current drawn in amp-hours. For those who want to pursue this course, a list of representative consumption values for familiar appliances appears in the Appendix towards the end of this book.

In this installation the standard 65W alternator has been replaced by a more powerful unit capable of 105A

Of course, much of this is guesswork. Refrigerators work harder when it's hot outside. Ditto autopilots when it's rough – or sometimes not at all with a human hand on the helm. While you might spend your evenings reading under a single light, visiting friends will be greeted with the whole saloon brightly lit – the gathering probably also increasing the load on that fridge as cold libations are dispensed. And so on. The truth is that accurate predictions are unattainable. At best, we can only get a rough approximation of how much electricity we need. The good news is that rough is good enough. We can take a more relaxed view of consumption by focusing on those other two issues – generation and storage.

But first we must understand 'charge acceptance rates' – by which we mean the maximum rate of charge a battery can take at any time. These vary with the type of battery, its capacity and, lastly, its state of charge. Back on page 32 we saw that a conventional lead-acid battery will accept a hefty current when partially discharged, but the rate of charge tails off as the chemical changes unfold and resistance builds. It has been determined that, when cycled between 50% and 80% of fully charged, liquid lead acid batteries have average acceptance rates of about 25% of their nominal C20 capacity.

Counting the amps – in and out

Both charge and discharge currents can be too large to be measured by conventional ammeters. Instead, a 'shunt' of very accurately callibrated low resistance is introduced into the circuit and the voltage drop (a matter of millivolts) is then measured across it. Knowing both the resistance and voltage drop, it's a simple matter for the meter to apply Ohm's Law (see page 9) to calculate the current flowing either into or out of the battery. Note the meter needs its own tiny power supply.

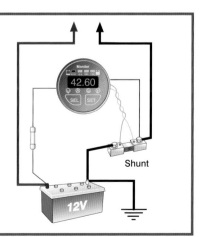

To put this in context, let's adopt a mid-size sailboat as an example. Its electrical system was specified by the builders: a 65A alternator serves a 220Ah flooded lead acid battery. Although the alternator is rated at 65A, that's only achieved at full speed and running reasonably cool (output falls with increase in temperature). So, at cruising revs on a steamy day it's better to assume 50A maximum to be on the safe side.

Now, the 50% to 80% span of this boat's battery capacity ranges from 100Ah to 176Ah – amounting to 76Ah in all. With a charge acceptance rate of 55A (220 x 25%) our 50A alternator would take just over 1h 22m to bring it back to 80% charge.

Which would be quite reasonable if you only consumed 76Ah per day.

Unfortunately, few modern sailboats achieve such frugality. A typical daily consumption for a typically gizmoed mid-size sailing cruiser might work out out at around 140Ah at sea (and perhaps 130Ah or so at anchor). To restore that 150Ah would mean the engine has to run 3 hours every day – not an attractive prospect for a sailboat.

The temptation is to add another battery in parallel, thus doubling the capacity. This clearly provides more storage and has the added benefit of increasing the charge acceptance rate to 110A (440 x 25%). Unfortunately, the alternator is still only capable of producing 50A so won't be able to take advantage of this.

So, what if we had stuck to the original battery and fitted a more powerful alternator – say, one with twice the real output: 100A? Now we have plenty of charge current but the battery's acceptance rate remains at 55A so there has been very little gained. All that extra power is wasted.

If this seems like the end of the trail, don't lose heart. Whereas our conventional lead-acid battery has a miserly 25% charge acceptance rate, gel types do much better at about 50% of rated capacity and AGMs will accept up to a staggering 100% (if cycled between 50% and 80%). If either were combined with the 100A alternator they would be recharged in less than half the time of the old battery. Similarly, the replenishment time for the 140Ah daily burden imposed by our yacht at sea would also be slashed.

Before we move on, it might be helpful to imagine a system where a 200A (again real output) alternator serves a 400Ah AGM bank – far from impracticable if there's space to accommodate them. With a 100% charge acceptance rate, the AGMs will take any charge current thrown at them, with lots to spare from other sources – a subject we shall be discussing in the next chapter. Thus equipped, our specimen yacht could mop up its daily 140Ah consumption with just over 40 minutes of engine power.

Audit the various electrical loads if you must, but you may find it more fruitful simply to engineer the best possible charging method you can fit to your boat and then deal with consumption as it comes. The best systems are those that match the various components with regard to charge acceptance rates. If space and weight aren't a problem, an oversized alternator charging a large conventional lead acid bank will do nicely. For more compact installations, gel or AGM batteries could be the answer.

Finally, resist any impulse to split large domestic banks in two. Remember: it's the size of the bank that increases acceptance rates, not the number.

WARNING: Repeatedly charging up to only 80% capacity is not the best regime for batteries. The closer you get to 100% the better.

CHAPTER 5

POWER FROM THE PLANET

Man has harnessed the forces of nature since prehistory. He still does. The technology might have changed, the scope widened by recent knowledge, but the principles remain the same. The wind has filled sails, both at sea and on windmills. Waterwheels have ground corn and powered primitive machinery. The sun dried early pots and bricks before kilns were invented.

And there's something immensely satisfying in employing commodities that are free. It's not often one gets something for nothing – nothing after you've paid for the gear, that is.

WIND TURBINES

Many early designs were 'generators' – basically electric motors running in reverse, producing DC currents by way of commutators. The modern trend, however, has been overwhelmingly towards 3-phase alternators, similar in many ways to engine types but using permanent magnets (rather than field windings) for excitation of the rotor. An internal rectifier converts the AC current to DC.

Although engineering quality might vary from model to model, claims of superior output can be questionable. This is because the factors that govern output are the same for all – the area swept by the blades and the rotation speed. In short, the longer the blades and the faster they whirl round, the more electricity you will get. In their efforts to out-gun their competitors, one or two manufacturers overcooked the speed option and a number of skippers found themselves receiving complaints from other boats – even banishment from marinas because, unfortunately, high revs inevitably produce lots of noise, and it has been irrefutably established that banshee wailing does not a good neighbour make. Thankfully, most wind turbines now incorporate some means, either mechanical or electrical, of taming their excesses before they become intolerable. Some are fitted with remote 'stop' switches that short out the stator coils, creating enough magnetic drag to bring them to a virtual halt.

CAUTION: Watch out for those blades. They can cause serious injury. Wind turbines should be mounted at a safe height, well above easy reach.

As can be seen from Figure 5:1, the output from a powerful generator becomes substantial as wind speed increases. At a relatively modest Force 7 you would see 350W to 400W (around 30A at 12V) and it would climb further if allowed to run away unchecked.

Whereas engine alternators are regulated by adjusting the power to their field coils, this isn't possible with permanent magnets. Yet some form of regulation is clearly necessary to defend the batteries from overcharge. Once the batteries are fully topped up, the most usual method dumps the excess power to a large ballast resistor (or two)

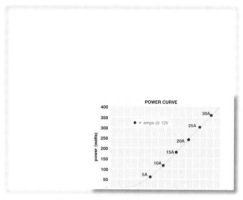

Figure 5:1

which dissipates the energy as heat. Another makes use of magnetic drag to reduce the generator to a sedate spin. Incidentally, don't assume because your wind turbine is turning it's actually charging. About 6 knots of apparent wind is necessary before the generator 'cuts in'. Also don't be disappointed if your wind turbine doesn't quite come up to the manufacturer's claims. These tend to assume optimum conditions and could even be mathematically derived outputs. Regard them as guides rather than absolute predictions.

What can they contribute?

Maximum outputs are all very well, but it's more important to know what can reasonably be expected over a 24 hour period. This depends on season and location. The mean wind speed for south-west Britain in July is about 10 knots. Referring to the graph (Fig 5:1 above) shows us that that particular generator would, in theory, yield about 45 watts – 3.75A at 12V, about 90Ah over the day. By contrast, if the same boat was in the West Indies in December (the high season) the trade winds might deliver 75 watts – a healthy 150Ah – enough to sustain many cruising boats without running their engines at all.

WATER POWERED GENERATORS

These use the same basic generator units as wind turbines, but the drive power comes from a turbine immersed in the water – either on a rigid strut or towed astern on a rope. These are popular for downwind passages where the apparent wind strength diminishes, but they're obviously useless at anchor or alongside. Recognising, their lack of versatility, at least three manufacturers offer convertible versions that can be converted from water to wind power.

The turbine unit (nearest) is connected by a rope to the generator mounted on the stern rail

SOLAR PANELS

Considering the enormous commercial and environmental potential tantalisingly presented by solar energy, it's not surprising that the field of 'photovoltaic' (PV) technology enjoys vigorous development.

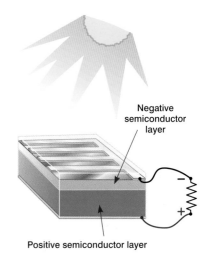

The majority of PV cells use silicon as their main constituent. In its pure form silicon is a poor conductor but, when deliberately 'doped' with impurities – gallium arsenide and indium phosphate being common – it becomes a 'semi-conductor' made up of a predominantly negative layer and a predominantly negative layer. All PV cells have at least two layers of each. When exposed to sunlight, 'photons' (light particles) nudge electrons loose from the negative layer and across the junction to the positive.

Silicon cells are those familiar iridescent dark blue ones and these divide into 'monocrystalline' (small individual cells) and 'polycrystalline' (larger cells). The first type is the most efficient – 15% as opposed to 13% but the bar is rising on these figures almost daily. Both are pretty good in sunny conditions.

However, crystalline silicon cells are expensive to produce, so manufacturers are looking at more economical alternatives. Non-crystalline amorphous silicon is used on flexible PV panels – relatively cheap, but only about 6% efficient so you need about twice the area for the same output..

If possible, solar panels should be mounted so they face directly towards the sun. In practice this is often impracticable so compromises have to be made.

All but the very smallest solar panels should be regulated to prevent damage to the batteries

A very promising newcomer doesn't use silicon at all, instead relying on copper indium diselenide (CuInSe2 or 'CIS'). CIS cells don't have quite the same peak output as the best silicon types but they respond to more of the light spectrum, meaning they function better over a broader range of conditions – dawn, dusk and cloudy, for instance. Judged over a variable day's output, they could actually be more productive. More importantly, they lend themselves to high-volume production, with all the cost savings that brings.

Obviously, the larger the array the more energy you can harvest. For a good quality panel, quoted figures indicate about 120W per square metre (much less for flexible panels) meaning a 10A current at 12V. But this is under ideal conditions, with a cloudless sky, a temperature of 25°C (output drops as PV cells become hot) and the panel pointing directly at the sun. You would probably only see this sort of performance at lower latitudes where the solar radiation is strongest (see Figure 5:2). However, summer days do lengthen the further north or south you stray so this at least partially compensates. As with wind generators, all but the smallest units should be regulated.

Overall, the average array packs nothing like the punch of most wind turbines but they can serve a very useful purpose. Working unattended and not prone to mechanical failure, they will maintain the battery charges levels for you when you're not on board.

Boats in the relatively windless Mediterranean might prefer solar panels whereas those in the windier UK would probably do better with a wind generators. Long distance cruisers often carry both – certainly a good combination in the Caribbean where there is both wind and sun.

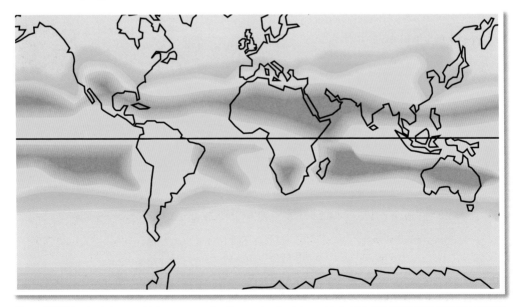

Figure 5:2 This chart shows which areas receive the most solar energy and which the least. The deepest orange is where the sun's effect is strongest, increasingly deepening blues where it's the weakest

CHAPTER 6

DISTRIBUTION CIRCUITS

So far we've dealt with the generation, control and storage of electricity – all functions embraced by the 'primary system'. The next step is to distribute the power to those appliances that depend upon it, and this responsibility falls to the 'secondary system'. The nerve centre of a secondary system is a switch panel – or 'panels' since there are often more than one – that allows individual circuits to be switched on or off at any time. If an electrical cable is asked to carry a current too great for its size it will overheat, possibly enough to set fire to the boat.

Fuses

Many switch panels also carry the fuses that protect each circuit, though they can be mounted remotely. So simple are fuses that it might seem insulting to explain how they work but … sorry about this … here goes all the same. Fuses provide a conductive weak link – a link that will melt if overloaded, breaking the circuit before it can become dangerously hot. All fuses are rated at the current (in amps) at which you would expect them to blow – with some allowance being made for the occasional modest surge. They come in two types: 'quick blow' and 'slow blow' with the latter tolerating surges the best. Unfortunately, the ratings can be unreliable. Being a fuse is not a lot of fun. Their role means they live constantly on the brink. The thermal stress they endure gradually weakens them, leaving their nominal ratings a youthful memory. With time they may die of natural causes, thereby disabling otherwise healthy circuits.

Circuit breakers

Fuses provide an inexpensive defence against short circuits or other overloads and they are often the best choice for open boats exposed to the weather, but they're rapidly being edged out by 'circuit breakers' (CBs). Circuit breakers bring many advantages: they can double as on-off switches; they don't destroy themselves in the line of duty; and their rated values can be believed with greater confidence. They operate in various ways.

A common approach is to combine a CB with an on-off switch.

- ■ Some have heat responsive bi-metallic strips that open pairs of contacts when they trip. These are called 'thermal CBs'.

- ■ Another technique uses solenoids to pull the contacts apart – 'magnetic CBs'.

- ■ A variation on the magnetic CB theme has hydraulically damped solenoids to introduce short delays. These fall into the group known as 'magnetic hydraulic CBs'.

But how they work isn't as important as what they do – more specifically how fast they react. Magnetic CBs trip almost instantaneously. You might think this a good idea but the fact is that they make twitchy shipmates, responding to transient current peaks that could safely be ignored. This leaves the other two.

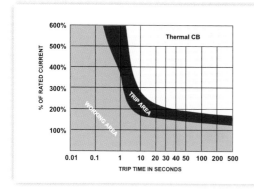 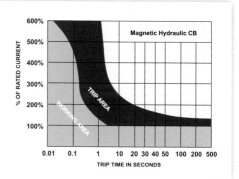

Figure 6:1

Compare the graphs in Figure 6:1. The important differences lie at the tops of the curves. At 600% above rated current value – without doubt an electrical crisis – the thermal CB trips after a short but significant delay. This could be long enough to melt the wire.

In the same circumstances the magnetic hydraulic CB comes to the rescue almost immediately. However, at lesser currents it still manages to be tolerant of brief surges. Not surprisingly it's this type that's generally preferred for distribution circuits.

All circuit breakers should be 'trip-free', meaning they can't be reset until existing faults have been corrected – a very important safety feature. If a CB trips, try to reset it once. If that fails, don't persist because there's clearly something wrong. Trace the circuit along its length until you find the problem.

Circuit wiring

Not everyone understands that fuses and circuit breakers are there to protect the cables, not the appliances. When it comes to designing circuits, it's very important that all cables be proportioned to deal with the maximum sustained loads they will bear. Unfortunately, the best laid plans are often upset by owners who later tap into the nearest available power source without realising they might be overloading the circuit. One example was the skipper who wondered why his cabin lights went dim every time his new refrigerator kicked in.

Quite apart from the fire risks associated with overloaded wiring, there's also the matter of 'voltage drop'. All cables offer resistance, and the thinner the cable, the longer the run and the greater the current, the more that voltage drop will be. A 10% drop is just acceptable for non-critical applications such as cabin lights but 5% would be better, particularly for heavier loads such as bilge pumps. Essential functions like navigation lights and electronic instruments should receive more generous consideration – a 3% voltage drop being the recommended limit.

Copper is a wonderful conductor – second only to silver in its conductivity and, of course, considerably more affordable. No surprise that it's the metal of choice for wiring and cables. The voltage drop for any installation is easily calculated, using the formula:

Voltage drop = 0.0164 x I x L/S

Where: I = load in amps
L = total length of cable to the load and back again
S = cross sectional area of conductor in square millimetres

Let's take an example: on a 12V system a masthead light representing a 2A load is mounted at a cable distance 15m from the distribution panel. Would a 1.5mm² conductor be enough?

% Voltage drop = 0.0164 x 2 x 30/1.5   % Voltage drop = 0.656V or 5.47%

So the answer is 'no', but it does give us a clue. Since the voltage drop is nearly twice what we're looking for, to double the conductor's area to 3mm² would do the trick. Unfortunately, there's no such cable size so we must use 4mm² (equivalent to American Wire Gauge [AWG] sizes 12 and 13). The voltage drop would now be a little over 2% – well within our limit.

The moral behind this example is that it never pays to skimp on cable sizes. The extra costs can always be justified in terms of both working efficiency and safety.

A table of recommended cable sizes for different loads and lengths is shown in the Appendix at the back of the book.

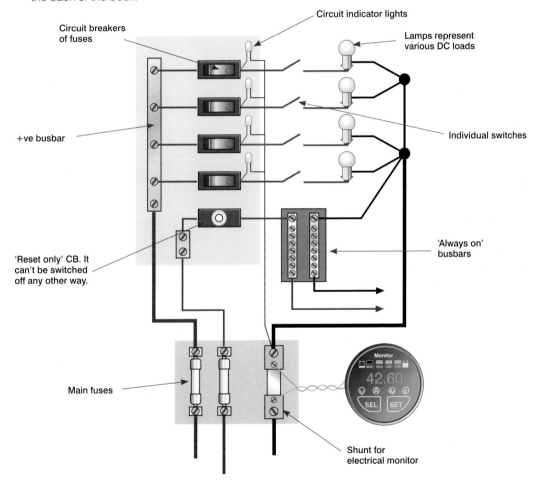

Fig 6:2 Basic distribution circuit

Negative returns

A basic distribution set-up is shown in Figure 6:2. Although every positive lead must snake all the way from the switchboard to the various appliances, this is unnecessary for all of the negative return leads. To reduce the number of wires returning to the main fuse (or CB) panel, it's common practice to connect groups of negatives to local junction boxes, bringing them all back as one along heavier gauge 'bus' cables as shown in the simplified illustration 6:3.

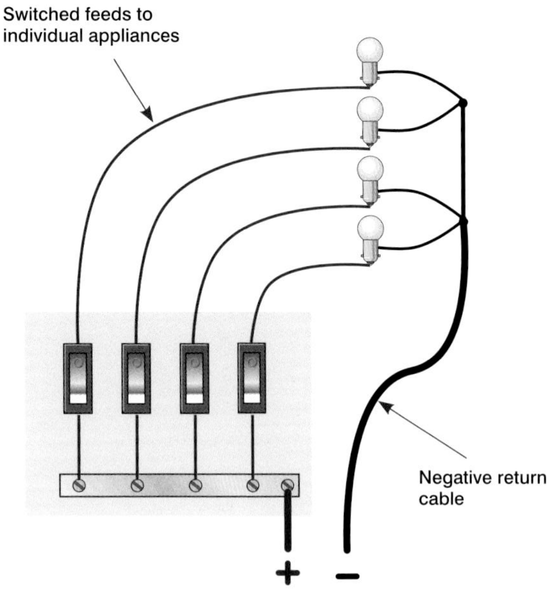

Distributed power supply

On larger vessels with complicated electrical systems, it's not unusual to find more than one DC switchboard, each controlling a group of functions – lighting, electronics, pumps etc. Each of these will be supplied by a central distribution panel which will deliver the power to the individual boards.

Switched feeds to individual appliances

Negative return cable

Figure 6:3

Always on

Sometimes called a 'maintained supply' the 'always-on' busbar and its supporting circuitry is a very useful facility on any boat. Its job is to provide a continuous electrical supply to equipment you want to leave active in your absence. These might include: automatic bilge pumps, burglar alarms and emergency radios.

Always-on circuits are connected directly to the batteries. That's to say they can't be isolated by a switch. Clearly they need some sort of protection against overload and this is usually a fuse or a 'reset only' circuit breaker – a type of CB which can't be tripped manually, only by a fault. Sometimes both are used, as shown in Figure 6:2.

Another benefit of having an always-on busbar is that it provides a convenient connection point for solar panels and wind generators.

Protection discrimination

If you were to trace a circuit from the power source to the appliance, you should find at least two overload protection devices along its length. These must be rated so the device closest to the load blows or trips first. If this was not the case, a fault in an appliance could blow a main fuse, thereby taking out part – or possibly all – of the distribution system. Again referring to Fig 6:2 the main fuse might be 50A while a lighting circuit CB could be 15A. No prizes for guessing which one goes first.

And that's as it should be.

Heavy load circuits

Such monsters as bow thrusters and electric windlasses need special treatment, since the currents they draw can be formidable. A windlass on a 12m sailboat is likely to draw about 80A – peaking well above that if the motor stalls under load (Figure 6:4).

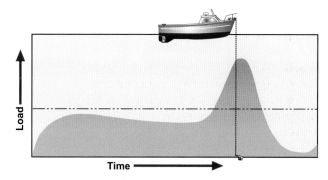

Figure 6:4 Windlass loads peak dramatically just before anchor breakout.

Currents of these magnitudes can't conveniently be handled by conventional switchgear. Instead, lighter circuits control the opening and closing of heavy duty relays – in principle a similar arrangement to that adopted for engine starter motors (page 25).

A cause of constant debate is whether to power these devices directly from the main service batteries or from a dedicated battery placed somewhere forward.

■ **The first option offers greater battery capacity to the load but means running heavy power cables up to the bow.**

■ **The cables for the second option can be lighter – but still must be substantial enough to carry the charge currents. Also, the issue of charge acceptance rates (see page 37) raises its ugly head. Finally, you will have added weight forward, rarely a good idea, particularly in a sailboat.**

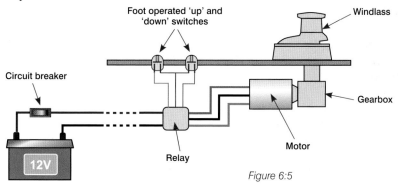

Figure 6:5

In most circumstances the engine should be running when thrusters and windlasses are in use. This allows the alternator to contribute to the power supply. Thrusters usually operate for no more than a few seconds, whereas windlasses might grind away for several minutes, placing sustained demands on the electrical system. It's very important that every installation must be carefully evaluated to make sure that each part of it is up to the job.

TIP: Windlasses run hot when heavily loaded. In difficult conditions it pays to recover the chain in short bursts to give the motor a chance to cool a little.

Up the stick

Overhead, mostly out of sight and with some components exposed to the weather, it's unsurprising that navigation and deck light systems can be troublesome. Which, of course, is unfortunate since access to much of it is awkward to say the least.

Happily, the circuitry is simple. Sailing yachts of less than 20m may carry a tricolour light (red, green and white) at the masthead, with a single lamp to illuminating all three segments, thereby saving electrical power and weight aloft. The tricolour is commonly combined in a single unit with an all-round anchor light. Such combination units are usually served by 3-core cables, connected so as to provide two individually switched and fused positive leads and a common negative return. A similar arrangement is often found powering combined steaming and deck working lights.

Cables running up the mast typically share that space with a number of halyards and other cordage, all brutally slapping and banging around inside as the boat heels. Ropes are accustomed to that sort of punishment but electrical cables aren't – at least not for long. The risk of damage to them is significant so, wherever possible, all mast wiring – including antenna and anemometer cables – should be protected by conduits.

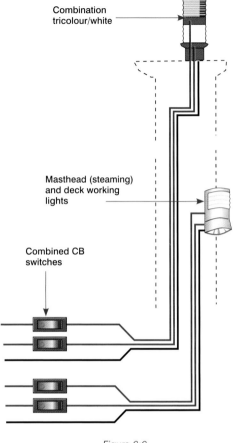

Figure 6:6

Other areas of risk occur where cables emerge from the mast or from tubular deck fittings such as pulpits and pushpits. Drilling holes in metal inevitably leaves sharp edges which, in time, can cut through insulation and cause short circuits. Wherever possible, protective rubber grommets should be used.

Another enemy of insulation is sunlight – more specifically, the UV end of the spectrum – which degrades PVC, leaving it powdery and brittle. Although most of the cable may be buried out of harm's way, it usually has to pop out somewhere, leaving it doubly exposed to attack from both weathering and abrasion. UV resistant cables are available but are rarely used on production boats where cost-cutting is a regrettable but predictable obsession.

TIP: Silicone grease or petroleum jelly (Vaseline) can help seal threaded assemblies but be careful not to contaminate the actual contacts which should always be left clean.

Deck glands and plugs

By definition, deck-stepped masts stop at deck level so some means has to be found to pass cables inside the boat to where they can be connected to the distribution circuit. In this there are basically two choices: waterproof plugs and socket sets where the cables are parted externally, and deck glands, where they are threaded through the deck with all connections being made at a junction box situated close to the mast step inside.

Both methods have their strengths and weaknesses. Waterproof plugs are certainly convenient but they must be of the highest quality to keep dampness at bay. Deck glands are generally simpler with the below-deck connections inherently enjoying much better shelter but the business of connecting and disconnecting the wiring is more of a hassle. Whereas, in the first instance, a mast could be lowered without anyone entering the boat, this would be impossible with deck glands. This may be a consideration if, say, work is entrusted to a boatyard.

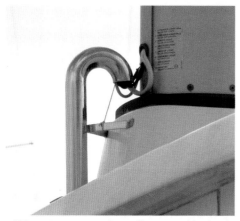

This system uses a rainproof 'swan neck' to lead the various cables below

Waterproof even if the decks are awash. The cables pass through these glands with all the connections being made below decks.

Cables and connectors

Domestic type cabling with single strand conductors is intended for static installations and has no place in the shuddering world of boats where the constant flexing might cause it to fatigue and break. The best choice is 'tinned' multi-strand cable where every copper strand is tin coated to protect it against corrosion. Unfortunately, this is expensive so many boat builders use un-tinned automotive wiring – a foolish and ill-judged economy when set against the overall cost of a boat. Many electrical faults owe their existence to such penny-pinching practices.

Another common source of problems are those wretched plastic terminal blocks – often called 'chocolate block' connectors – the vast majority of which have rust-prone plated steel clamping screws . For some applications their use can be justified but care must be taken that their screws are of brass, not steel (test with a magnet if you're not sure) and that they are adequately protected against moisture, perhaps with a smear of silicone grease.

Wherever possible use marine grade junction boxes, bus bars and junction posts. There are a number of companies specialising in such products.

On crimps and crimping

It's asking for trouble simply to strip off the insulation and use the end of a bare wire to make a connection – though sometimes this is unavoidable when connecting to appliances such as cabin lights. However, there are no excuses when it comes to the general circuitry.

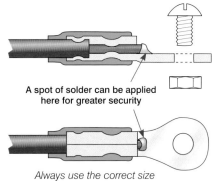

A spot of solder can be applied here for greater security

Always use the correct size crimps for the wire

Cable runs should end in crimped connectors protected with heat-shrunk tubing if there's any risk of water ingress. Wherever possible use a tubing coated internally with an adhesive that melts to forms a seal. Not all do. Some connectors come fitted with heat shrink sleeves, but the tubing can be bought separately in handy lengths and of various diameters and colours. The shrinking is usually done with an electric heat gun.

The best tool for crimping is a ratchet type crimper – to ensure compatibility, preferably from the same manufacturer as the crimps themselves. Unfortunately, in the real world there are many non-standard sized crimps to be found – not all of which can be satisfactorily compressed by any one ratchet crimper because of mismatches between jaw and crimp sizes. There are also metric and non-metric sized crimps and it's important you use the correct crimper. Although not ideal, in some circumstances the cheaper crushing type crimpers can sometimes do a better job. Always give the terminal a good tug to make sure the joint is sound. If extra security is required you can lightly solder the end of the cable where it emerges from the crimp.

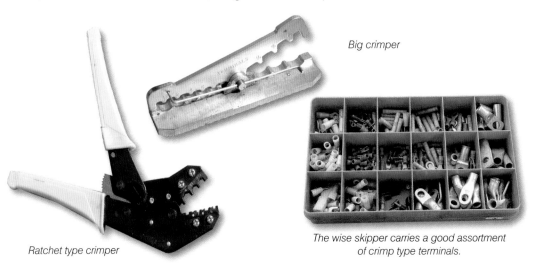

Big crimper

Ratchet type crimper

The wise skipper carries a good assortment of crimp type terminals.

SOLDERING:

Although solder is widely used inside electronic appliances, it's not recommended for general circuitry because soldered joints form 'structural hardspots' that, with movement, can fatigue and fracture.

CHAPTER 7

AC POWER

Small to mid-size boats can operate perfectly adequately on low voltage systems, but there's a trend – some would say unfortunate – to insist on all the comforts of home while afloat. Such landlubberly devices as microwaves, immersion water heaters, wide screen TVs and air conditioning are gaining favour – and all demand more power than 12 volts can realistically provide. The only way to satisfy their greed is to feed them the sort of fare they would expect ashore: namely an alternating current (AC) of somewhere between 110V – 240V.

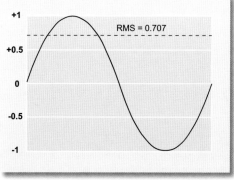

Before we look at how this can be achieved, let's dwell a while on AC theory – a subject we touched on in another context back on page 28. To recap: an alternating current is produced when a magnet is rotated within a coil of wire. The output emerges as a sinesoidal wave rising and falling about zero. The faster the magnet rotates, the greater the voltage and current (and, incidentally, the frequency – i.e. the number of complete cycles per second, measured in hertz (Hz)).

So, we have a situation where the voltage rises from zero to a peak in one direction, then falls back to zero and does the same in the other direction. In such fluctuating circumstances how can we define the effective 'voltage', that's to say the magnitude of benefit we can expect to get from it? The solution lies in what's known as the 'root mean square' (RMS) which for practical purposes we can take to be 0.707 (the square root of one half) times the peak voltage. For instance:

RMS value = 340V x 0.707 = 240V

Which is a representative domestic AC voltage across Europe.

AC current showing Root Mean Square of voltage

Resistive and inductive loads

Knowing the RMS allows us to use the same equations as we do for DC but only where 'resistive' loads are concerned. When it comes to 'inductive' loads the equations cannot be relied upon. Inductive loads may need heavier cables and more overload protection than the simple sums would indicate. So, we need to understand the difference between the two types of load.

■ Resistive loads convert current into other forms of energy. Light bulbs and heater elements are good examples. DC equations can be used to calculate AC current and power values if the RMS voltage is used.

■ Inductive loads employ magnetic fields – electric motors and solenoids, for instance. Any device that moves probably presents an inductive load, but this isn't a dependable test. Transformers, for instance, are conspicuously static. The starting loads for heavy electric motors need particular consideration.

Shore power

Although relatively few boats regularly use AC at sea, the majority take advantage of it when alongside. After all, if the marina operator is thoughtful enough to provide this service, why not accept it willingly? Why not indeed. The benefits are many though they are not without risks – both to human health and your boat.

The story starts with the local electricity company supplying 3-phase AC power (typically 415V) to the marina. This is divided into 240V single-phase and distributed to the various pontoons where 3-pin electrical sockets, mounted on pedestals and often metered, are spaced so as to be accessible to neighbouring boats. The sockets are normally rated at 15A – enough for most purposes but not for very heavy loads such as household type stoves which can draw as much as 40A.

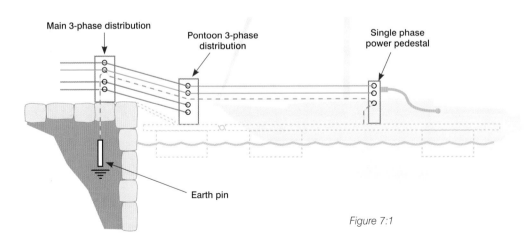

Main 3-phase distribution

Pontoon 3-phase distribution

Single phase power pedestal

Earth pin

Figure 7:1

The three conductors that carry the power to the socket are 'live', 'neutral' and 'earth'. As can be seen from Figure 7:1, the neutral and earth are linked together ashore (but never on the boat!) and 'earthed' (or 'grounded', it means the same thing) to a pin or plate buried underground. This is to maintain the neutral at 'earth potential' – i.e. zero volts.

The purpose of the earth wire is to provide an escape path for any 'fault' currents to be conducted safely from the boat. In theory, the shore supply's earth should be sufficient but, regrettably, there are so many links in the chain where resistance can occur – poor or corroded connections being regular culprits – that you can't take its integrity for granted. An electrical leak will seek the easiest route to earth, and that could be via your body! So, how does the AC power come on board?

Extension cables

The simplest, and perhaps most familiar, use of AC involves hooking an extension cord into the pontoon to allow a charger to feed the various battery banks. Thereafter the boat runs entirely on its DC system. Simple it may be, with few opportunities for faults, but some sensible precautions should still be taken to make it as safe as possible.

A true story

A true story illustrates why care is so necessary. A young man was preparing a Mediterranean charter yacht for sea. The boat was moored stern-to in the local manner. To power the vacuum cleaner and polishers used in the rather frantic titivation (new charterers were due any minute) an electrical cable had been strung from ashore. Unknown to anyone its insulation had worn through where it crossed the aluminium toerail, exposing the live conductor. Everything attached to the toerail – including the pushpit – was now energised.

People had been boarding the boat through a transom gate all day without incident but our young man was unlucky. While polishing the pushpit he steadied himself by grabbing the stainless steel steering wheel. This was all the current was waiting for – a path to earth, through the steering linkage and down the rudder stock. Worse still for him, the shock travelled from arm to arm, across the victim's chest, by far the most lethal course. At these voltages a current as low as 60mA can cause ventricular fibrillation and death. Wearing rubber soled shoes on a GRP deck, he may have been safe if he had not touched the wheel. Then the extension cable might simply have been coiled away and used another day.

Thankfully he survived, but only after vigorous resuscitation and several days in a coma.

Make no mistake:
AC CURRENTS ARE POTENTIALLY LETHAL

Residual Current Devices (RCDs)

Our man was doubly unlucky, for there was a bit of kit inside the power pedestal that should have spared him the worst – if not all – effects of the shock, had it functioned properly. Such a gadget is known as a 'residual current device' (RCD) or 'earth link circuit breaker' (ELCB) and there would almost certainly have been one immediately upstream of the power socket.

RCDs rely on a simple but elegant principle. In a closed circuit the current remains constant throughout its length – in short, what goes in one end has to come out the other. If it doesn't there must be some electrical leakage somewhere. In an RCD unit the live and neutral conductors pass through a torroidal (ring) transformer which senses their magnetic fields. If all is well these fields will cancel out each other – i.e. amount to zero. But if a leakage causes an imbalance, the RCD will spot the difference and trip the circuit to make it safe.

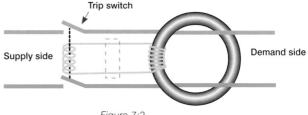

Figure 7:2

RCDs are rated at the current differential at which they will operate (30mA being typical for human protection) and the trip speed (30–100msecs of 'break time'). They are sometimes combined with overload protection circuit breakers whereupon they become knows as RCBOs – a mercifully abbreviated acronym for Residual Current Breaker for Overcurrent Protection.

Portable RCDs

It's a sad fact, but we can't rely absolutely on whatever safety provisions come built into the shore supply. RCDs may be defective and the conductivity of the earth wire could have been compromised – it's impossible to tell from the outside.

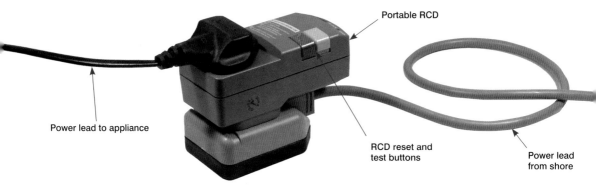

For those using extension cords, a useful safety precaution is to fit a portable RCD of the type shown above. These are commonly used with such devices as electric hedge trimmers and mowers. Ideally, they should be fitted at the power source – i.e. at the socket – but they are unlikely to be weatherproof and, anyway, domestic and marina type plugs and sockets are almost invariably incompatible. This means the RCD will probably have to be at the onboard end of the cord – by no means ideal but a lot better than nothing.

GOING TO GROUND – GAINS AND PAINS

Given that the conductive quality of a marina's ground may be questionable, there's a powerful argument for each boat having its own AC ground or earth. This is a view supported by a number of authoritative bodies, such as the British Marine Electronics Association (BMEA), the American Boat and Yacht Council (ABYC) and ISO. It also finds itself given required status within the requirements of the EU's Recreational Craft Directive.

But fitting a ground plate brings both problems and dangers – including the possibility of electrocuting nearby swimmers by energising the surrounding water! In trying to strike a balance between gain and pain, those same organisations also advise that the AC ground be electrically linked to the DC negative, though this is not recommended in some quarters. The link has the advantage of preventing potential differences between the two that could cause electrolytic corrosion (see page 62). Unfortunately, with the two systems directly linked, there comes the possibility that an AC fault could energise the supposedly 'safe' DC system up to a dangerous AC voltage.

The pros and cons continue to be hotly debated but improvements in the protection offered by RCD technology are giving rise to the many would say heretical counterview that boats whose AC comes solely from shore power may not need ground plates at all (Figure 7:3). However, there's no disputing that earthing is an essential safety measure at sea – of which more shortly.

Figure 7:3 shows a simple but permanent installation where the AC shore supply is used 'raw' to power onboard appliances, while at the same time feeding the battery charger to sustain DC power. An RCD stands guard over the electrical source.

This still remains a relatively elementary set-up, but it does serve to illustrate the basic principles. The reality is that, as average boat sizes increase and demands for onboard comfort gather pace, AC systems are becoming more and more complicated. Indeed, in the very largest yachts, AC might take over the central role entirely. For obvious reasons this is not a subject that impacts on many of us.

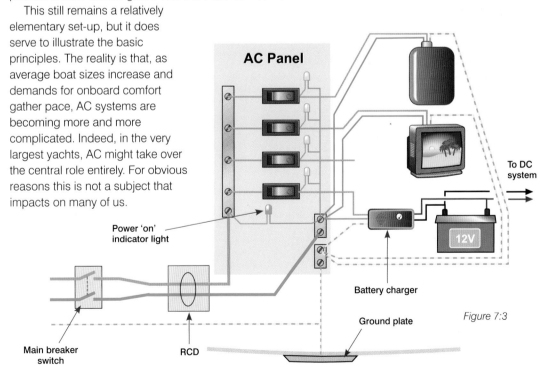

Figure 7:3

RYA Electrics Handbook

Reverse polarity

It's an astonishing fact that the polarity of shore power cannot be relied upon. Since AC appliances don't care about polarity, operating contentedly regardless of which cables are live or neutral, many marinas feel free to adopt slaphappy standards.

The results can be very dangerous. Switches, fuses and single-pole CBs should always be in the live side of a circuit – and of course wouldn't be if the neutral was live instead. Many boats have a polarity test facility built into their AC panels. An inexpensive alternative is a portable plug type tester that will also reveal any earth or neutral faults.

Some AC panels have switches that will correct reverse polarity. If not, a simple remedy is to swap the live and neutral connections at the plug. If moving from marina to marina it might pay to make up a short 'reversing lead' (above) that will do the same job without all the hassle.

The polarity was found to be incorrect on this power pedestal. The short white lead corrects this fault by swapping the live and neutral connections.

Incorrect polarity light

This simple system can warn you if the shore polarity is incorrect. Since earth and neutral are both connected to ground the potential difference between them should be zero volts and the light won't show. But if the AC supply has been wrongly connected, the light will be energised and you will know something is wrong.

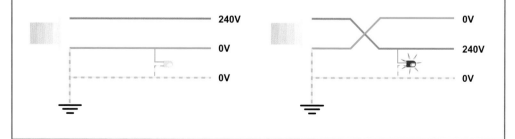

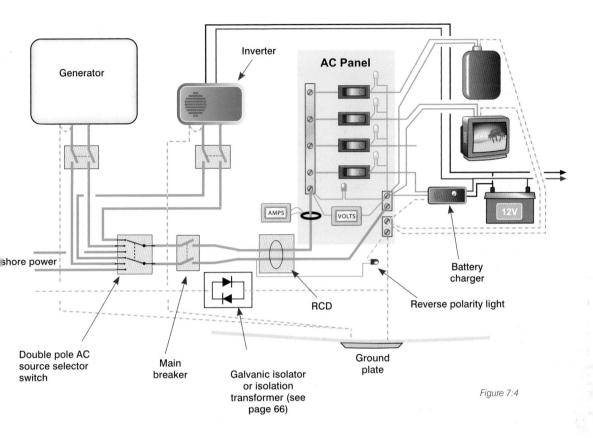

Inverter

AC Panel

Generator

AMPS

VOLTS

12V

shore power

Battery charger

Reverse polarity light

Double pole AC source selector switch

Main breaker

Galvanic isolator or isolation transformer (see page 66)

RCD

Ground plate

Figure 7:4

Figure 7:4 Shows a more elaborate installation that includes the means to produce AC at sea. Additional refinements are meters monitoring volts and amps, an 'incorrect polarity' warning light and a 'galvanic isolator' – a device which features prominently in the next chapter.

AC UNDER WAY

The sheer convenience of having access to domestic voltage AC has persuaded many boat owners that what's good for life alongside would also be handy at sea. And it is. These very words took shape on a laptop screen aboard my boat anchored off a sunny Ionian island.

The sources of such power are various. You could fit an appropriate alternator to the main engine, for example, but this would mean running the engine at constant revs while it generates. More practicable solutions are:

- An 'inverter' that converts the boat's low voltage DC to mains voltage AC.

- An independent AC motor-generator unit – almost invariably diesel fuelled in larger sizes, but smaller, often portable sets usually run on petrol.

Let's look at those individually.

Inverters

These are the obvious choice when AC consumption is relatively light. Early inverters were electromechanical with magnetically operated switches buzzing back and forth to reverse the polarity of the current. These days the oscillations are achieved electronically. A solid state oscillator converts the DC to AC and the voltage is then raised to 230V (or 110V) by way of a transformer.

The outputs emerge as waveforms whose profiles fall into one of three categories, starting with the simplest and least expensive:

■ **Square wave**

■ **Modified square wave**

■ **Sine wave**

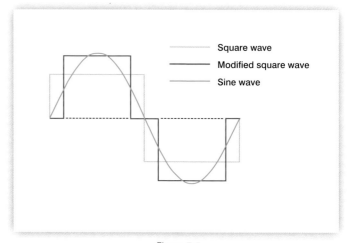

Figure 7:5

The square wave type is too primitive to be useful for most purposes which leaves the other two.

Modified square wave (also called a quasi sine wave units) are mid-priced inverters that will run most equipment but can struggle with inductive loads, meaning anything involving electric motors, particularly variable speed devices like power tools and washing machines. Harmonic distortion can also cause unwanted interference in sensitive electronic equipment such as televisions and audio systems.

Pure sine wave inverters occupy the top end of the market and very closely mimic the quality of power source you would expect at home. In short, they will run anything.

> ❗ **WARNING:** Different AC sources should never be allowed to run simultaneously. Steps must be taken to ensure that when one source – say the shore supply – is connected, other sources are isolated, usually by means of double-pole selector switch.

The size of the inverter will depend on how much power you require (see the panel below for some representative AC ratings). But need isn't the only consideration. It's also important to remember that your DC system must be capable of supporting whatever loads are asked of it. You can't expect a monster inverter to be fed from a modest battery bank.

The process of converting DC to AC involves some loss of power, but good quality inverters are pretty efficient with around 90% being typical of many.

The DC draw for any given load can be calculated thus:

$$\text{DC draw} = \frac{\text{AC power (watts) x active hours per 24hrs}}{\text{DC volts x inverter efficiency}}$$

Now let's assume our skipper is cruising under sail and hankers for running hot water. He has a calorifier with a 240V AC immersion heater drawing 1.25kW when active – about 3hrs per day he reckons, to heat enough for showers for the crew, washing up, etcetera. Plugged into our equation this means:

$$\text{DC draw} = \frac{1.25 \times 1000 \times 3}{12 \times 0.9} = \frac{3750}{10.8} = 347\text{Ah per day}$$

Wow! And to this must be added the 150Ah per day he normally draws from his DC system in the general operation of his boat. Clearly this is an extremely discouraging result, almost certainly taking the overall DC consumption beyond sustainable levels.

So it's not just what you want that determines inverter size, but also what you can afford in terms of DC power. Inverters are great at powering relatively light loads, or heavier loads for short periods of time, but if you want a sustained and substantial AC supply you need something more muscular – an independent motor generator would do nicely.

AC ratings

Appliance	Power rating (Watts)
TV	110
Microwave	850
Electric kettle	2000
Toaster	1000
Vacuum cleaner	1000
Hair dryer	2000
Computer	40

Inverters are often combined with battery chargers and are commonly known as 'combi' units. This makes both economic and practical sense, since some of the components and circuitry are common to both.

Motor-generators

Either petrol or diesel fuelled – the choice often depends upon the primary propulsion fuel – considerable strides have been made to make 'gensets' smaller, lighter, quieter and more efficient. Basically, a combustion engine spins an AC generator at a constant speed, outputting either 220-240V AC or 110V AC at 60 or 50Hz respectively.

Small boat generators are nearly always single phase, and their output is customarily rated in kVA (kilovolt amps), a fact that deserves explanation since volts times amps usually emerges as watts (so you might expect a kVA to equal a kW).

Generator manufacturers face a dilemma. They don't know in advance what kind of loads their generators will face. A panel on page 52 introduced us to 'inductive' loads and conveniently dodged a full explanation. Since it's this type of load that gives generators a headache, it's time to tackle this subject in more depth.

Such devices as electric motors present inductive loads that (unlike resistive loads) can cause the voltage and current AC waveforms, which are normally superimposed (in phase), to move out of phase with each other. When the two are in phase, multiplying volts by amps in the usual way makes it possible to predict watts at any point on the waveform. This isn't so easy when they're out of step so, to compensate for the loss of efficiency and hefty starting loads, a 'power factor' (PF) is applied – usually about 0.8 – and the apparent power indicated in kVA instead of kW.

Therefore:

$$\frac{\text{real power (kW)}}{\text{PF}} = \text{apparent power (kVA)}$$

To demonstrate the implications, let's assume one of the loads is a 1hp (0.75kW) electric motor having a PF of 0.9. Applying the above formula gives us:

$$\frac{0.75}{0.90} = 0.83\text{kVA}$$

So, manufacturers rate their generators according to whatever total load (in kVA) they can safely accept without overheating. With purely resistive loads, such as heating elements, there are no phase distortions so power factors don't apply. For them, 1kW equals 1kVA and can added to the other loads without modification.

TIP: Avoid firing up motor-generators while heavy loads are connected to it. It's much kinder to allow the machinery time to warm up before burdening it too brutally.

Automatically controlled generators

Many gensets can be set to sense battery charge states and will start automatically when predetermined discharge levels are reached. A nice idea, but you may not think so when they roar to life at night.

Working in tandem

Generators and inverters can often split the workload between them. For example, our skipper with the immersion heater could have had the generator take care of heating his water while charging the batteries via the charger at the same time.

Which takes us neatly on to...

Battery chargers

Gone are the days when a battery charger was no more than a lumpy transformer and a crude rectifier stuffed into a metal box. Today's 'switch mode' units are entirely electronic and are more efficient and much lighter than their predecessors. Their output is usually multi-stage (bulk, absorption, float, then coping with DC loads), in a very similar manner to the smart alternator controllers we met way back on page 32. Some chargers rely on relatively simple timers to control the charge regime, others use microprocessors to monitor the battery state and optimise the regime accordingly.

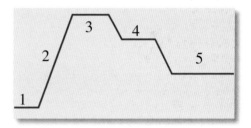

Multi-staged charging regimes get the best from your batteries

The sophistication or otherwise that every battery charger brings to its task tends to be reflected in its price. Generally, the more you pay, the more bells and whistles you get. Purchase costs also rise with increases in output – an important consideration since charging capability should be matched to the capacity of the battery bank. Big banks demand powerful chargers if they're to be replenished in a reasonable time. On the other hand it's possible to ruin a smaller bank by trying to charge it too rapidly.

So, how potent a charger should you buy? Well, advice differs but a charge current (amps) of somewhere around 25% to 45% of the service bank's capacity (in Ah) is reckoned to be about right.

A FRUITLESS STRATEGY: There's no point in attempting to top up your batteries by connecting a battery charger to an inverter. Since a typical inverter is only about 90% efficient, you will incur a 10% net loss in the transaction. With combined charger/inverter units the internal switching makes this ludicrous trick impossible.

CHAPTER 8

CORROSION PROTECTION

It's impossible to get to grips with electrically promoted corrosion (as distinct from that caused by oxidation, such as rusting) without appreciating the extent, vigour and unpredictability of the electrical frenzy that surrounds us. Our boats are assembled from materials of varying potential. We then launch them into a soup, also of varying potential, and – as if that wasn't enough – teeming with stray leakage currents we can neither see nor easily measure. If ever there was a case of chaos from within and chaos from without, this is it.

Before we move on let's clarify a widespread misunderstanding. In the corrosion context, the words 'galvanic' and 'electrolytic' are frequently assumed to be interchangeable, whereas they actually mean entirely different things.

Galvanic corrosion occurs when dissimilar metals having different potentials are immersed in an electrolyte and connected by a conductor (Fig 8:1). This forms a 'galvanic cell', a very simple form of battery in which the negative 'cathode' remains intact and the positive 'anode' is eaten away, a current being produced in the process. A bronze propeller on a stainless steel shaft is one example, a stainless steel stanchion in an aluminium socket is another.

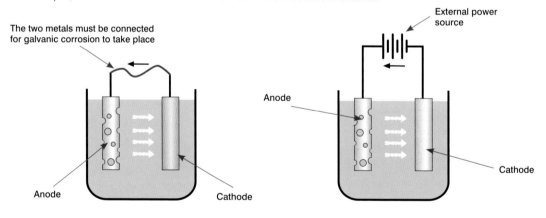

Figure 8:1 Galvanic corrosion   *Figure 8:2 Electrolytic corrosion*

By contrast, electrolytic corrosion results from an electric current from an external source (often accidental leakage). In this case the two immersed metals can either be different or the same, since the potential difference between them is imposed by the current, with the identities of anode and cathode being determined by the polarity of that current (Fig. 8:2). The damage caused by electrolytic action can occur rapidly, because both the currents and potential difference can be high. And, of course, it's always the anode that takes the hammering.

Let's stick with galvanic corrosion for now.

Mixing the metals

The panel below shows the 'galvanic scale' – a selection of metals, each of them occupying a specific place in a strictly hierarchical system. At the noble, most cathodic end of our scale is black-hearted graphite (not a metal but warrants inclusion as a conductive material – think carbon fibre which has a very similar atomic structure) followed by those swanky elements, gold and platinum. Looking to the lowliest, anodic end of the scale we see that zinc and then magnesium preside over the most ignoble orders.

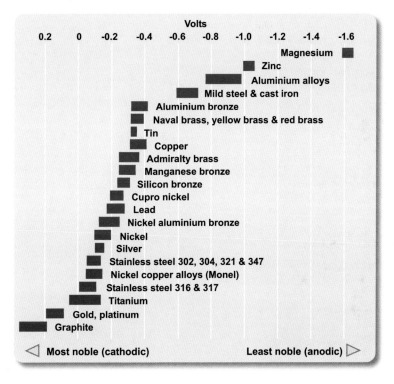

There's nothing arbitrary about their rank. Their positions are assigned in an order that shows how each metal would fare relatively if connected to another metal and immersed in a known electrolyte. The electrolyte in this case is flowing seawater, and lest you think the word 'flowing' is technical hair-splitting, you should know that the potentials of some metals – stainless steels, for instance – will change significantly, depending upon whether the water is aerated or not. Incidentally, temperature also has an effect.

To demonstrate the significance of the galvanic scale, let's consider a couple of examples. The first involves securing an aluminium alloy fitting by means of stainless steel (grade 304) bolts – a very common combination. From the scale we can see that the potential of the aluminium is about -0.9V and that of the bolts -0.1V. This means that the potential difference between them is 0.8V – in galvanic terms quite a lot. Because the aluminium is 'less noble' than the stainless steel, it becomes the anode in this particular galvanic cell and will suffer accordingly. The stainless steel, being the cathode, will remain unharmed.

Now let's use those same bolts to secure a titanium fitting – by no means unknown on racing boats. Titanium's average potential is about -0.05V so in its relationship with stainless steel (-0.1V) there's a potential difference between them of 0.05V. This time the stainless steel finds itself in the less noble position so becomes the anode to the titanium's cathode – meaning that in the galvanic arm wrestling that will follow, the stainless steel will get its comeuppance.

There are two points to be gained from these examples:

1. The roles of anode and cathode are not unconditional (except for those at the extreme ends of the scale) but change according to the relationships between any two metals. It's the direction of current flow that determines which is which.

2. The greater the potential difference, the more vigorous will be the galvanic activity. In our first example (stainless steel and aluminium) there was 0.8V between them, so significant galvanic corrosion can be expected. In the second example there was only 0.05V and the threat of corrosion is negligible. This means that, when combining metals, the closer they are on the galvanic scale the more comfortably they will be able to live together.

So, what can we do about it? Well, fortunately there's quite a bit we can do to limit the damaging effects.

Sacrificial anodes

Galvanic corrosion can be countered by deliberately introducing a strongly anodic metal which sacrifices itself to protect objects more cathodic than itself. The chosen sacrifice – usually of zinc or, less commonly, aluminium – comes in various forms, as can be seen in the photos below. Some are bolted to the hull and bonded internally to vulnerable components (engines, shafts and P-struts being notable) and some are attached directly to the object they seek to protect (shafts, trim tabs etc).

Sacrificial anode

Both of the metals become cathodes relative to the anode

Hull anode

Shaft anode

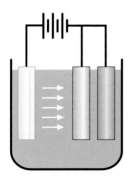

Impressed current

Yet another method employs deliberate electrolytic intervention. The lowly zinc is replaced by a nobler (meaning more cathodic) metal and a small current is introduced to counter the direction of the galvanic flow. Impressed current systems are very popular on large commercial vessels, where the frequent replacement of anodes is impracticable. On pleasure craft they are used chiefly to protect highly vulnerable machinery such as aluminium alloy encased drive legs and jet drives.

Dezincification

An insidious form of galvanic corrosion attacks manganese bronze components, such as propellers. Proper bronze is an alloy of copper and tin but manganese bronze is a mix of copper, zinc (about 40%) and a small amount of manganese and should more rightly be described as brass. Now, copper and zinc are a fair way apart on the galvanic scale so it should come as no surprise to find that the anodic zinc gradually becomes depleted leaving soft and powdery copper behind. For props and through-hull fittings, aluminium bronze is a much better choice. Stronger and more corrosion resistant, it has a much higher copper content which might even, as a bonus, help deter fouling organisms.

Planning any cathodic protection system should be done thoughtfully and with restraint. Isolated components such as bronze seacocks (when secured with bronze bolts or attached to bronze through hull fittings) shouldn't be connected, because to do so might create galvanic cells where none existed before.

Anodes will also provide protection against electrolytic attack but the length of time they can hold out against such assaults depends on the strength of the currents involved. Once any anodes have been depleted, the most anodic components that remain will be targeted next.

And it needn't be your fault. Even if you're scrupulous about guarding your own electrical systems against leakage (see page 78 for tests), you can still fall victim to the carelessness or misfortune of others. Marinas are notorious breeding grounds for rogue currents, either from neighbouring boats or from the pontoons themselves. Other people's problems can become your own – unseen and often expensive.

WARNING: Care should be taken not to over-protect wooden hulled vessels. Traditional boatbuilding timbers such as oak and mahogany are naturally acidic but localised galvanic action can make them alkaline, destroying the lignin that binds the fibres together (the process is known as delignification). Softening of planking around anodes and seacocks is a very common fault caused by this process.

Earth loops

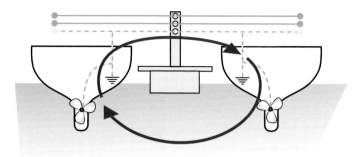

Figure 8:3 shows two yachts, both properly connected to the shore power. In compliance with recommended practice, each has its AC and DC grounds bonded together. Neither is actually drawing power from the pontoon but this doesn't matter. Even with their systems dormant, the earth wire continues to link them together, binding them into

Figure 8:3 Even if not using any shore power, boats can be connected by the earth wire.

a galvanic relationship in which the most anodic boat (for whatever reason) will suffer damage. Leakage currents will make the situation even worse.

The temptation for boat owners is to break the loop by simply disconnecting the shore AC earth wire. But this is not without its risks even if the supply is protected by an onboard RCD – an ABSOLUTELY ESSENTIAL safety measure anyway. A much safer strategy is to block the path for tiny DC currents to escape while still allowing full AC fault currents to run safely to earth. There are two ways of achieving this. They are:

■ **ISOLATION TRANSFORMERS: Although heavy and relatively expensive, these should be seriously considered for larger vessels with elaborate AC systems and those with conductive hulls – i.e. aluminium, steel or carbon fibre composite. Here there's no direct connection with the shore supply. The power is transferred by induction from one coil to another. A boat ground plate is necessary to maintain** the neutral at earth potential but at least there are no polarity problems since isolation transformers don't care which way round the shore power arrives.

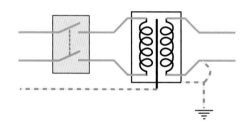

■ **GALVANIC ISOLATOR: Lighter and less costly, these are a good choice for simpler systems. A pair of diodes are arranged in parallel on the earth. An AC current will pass straight through – in or out – while a low voltage DC current will find one diode barring its way entirely while the voltage drop (typically about 0.7V) across the other diode will negate its effect if coming in the opposite direction. If that isn't** enough, the diodes can be wired in series to double their effect.

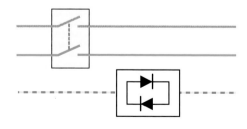

CHAPTER 9

DRAIN BRAIN

Being hooked up to a limitless supply of AC alongside can promote habits that become glaringly inappropriate at sea. Electrical extravagance may not be a problem for marina hoppers who plug into shore power at day's end, but for voyagers and those who spend long spells at anchor reliant on their 12V DC systems, the issue is crucial. Apart from the power harnessed from the wind and sun, your resources are finite. It follows that the less you use, the longer you will enjoy the benefits.

Fortunately, technology is moving towards us. Granted we're increasingly tempted by electrical gadgetry but at least these modern offerings in the main use the power more efficiently than the clanking beasts of yesterday. One area – that of lighting – now affords astonishing savings in consumption.

LEDs offer huge savings in electrical consumption. This anchor light draws only a fifth of its incandescent equivalent.

Light emitting diodes (LEDs)

LEDs are similar to diodes we have met earlier but have been doped in such a way as to emit light when a current is passed through them. Compared to incandescent lamps their power consumption is astonishingly low – some 30-60 milliwatts (mW) per individual LED being typical. However, the light from a single unit is rarely enough so they are usually assembled into clusters to provide more useful outputs. Even so, they will consume only a fraction of their conventional forerunners. For example, a legal (visible at 2nm) LED anchor light will only draw about 2W compared with the 10W we've been accustomed to for so long. That's a saving in power of over 80% – 1.3Ah instead of 17Ah over an 8 hour night!

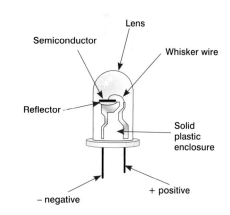

Similar savings can be had from the interior lighting but many people don't like the ghastly 'tales from the crypt' hues cast by some LED cabin lights. They usually think of the light as 'cold' which is actually the reverse of what's happening. Think of the difference between red hot and white hot and you will understand why this is so.

Visible light ranges from bright red to deep blue (Fig 9:1) and any hue on that scale can be defined by its 'colour temperature' in 'kelvins' (K). Confusingly, what we perceive as hot reds have low colour temperatures while blues are much hotter. Bright noontime sunlight falls somewhere in the middle at about 5000K while ordinary household lamps are much cooler at maybe 2700K.

So, it's all about perception. We've become as accustomed to the yellow hues of incandescent lamps as our ancestors were to candlelight (1000K). So-called 'white' LED lights span the 3000K to 6000K colour temperature range. It's up to you to pick what suits you best.

Other useful ploys for conserving your electrical power are:

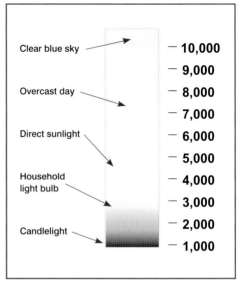

Figure 9:1

- ■ Remember Peukert (page 22). The rate of discharge has a profound influence on battery capacity. The faster you use it, the less capacity you will have. For example, a pair of cabin lights lit for one hour will deplete the battery more than a single light will in two hours.

- ■ For a boat at sea, electrical consumption tends to peak after sunset before the boat settles into its night watch regime. This is a good time to run the engine to top up the batteries, because the alternator will take up the extra loads while it's charging.

- ■ Fit foot or hand water pumps in the galley and heads and switch off the electric pressure system when not alongside. Both electricity and water consumption will be reduced and it encourages awareness of how much is being consumed.

■ Refrigerators are heavy guzzlers of power – more so if the insulation is inadequate, as is the case on many production boats. 100mm thick is ideal. Also, a well stocked fridge holds its temperature better than an empty one so try and keep it as full as is practicable. Even top loading fridges – the preferred type, since the air inside is denser than the warmer air outside and will fall out of a front-opener every time someone cracks the door open – should be opened as infrequently as possible. This may call for a bit of forward thinking. For instance, at breakfast time take the milk, butter and anything else you might want out at the same time, then return them together once you've finished. If you want a cold beer make sure you're not the only one so you don't have to go back and lift that lid again.

Above all, communicate the need for electrical stinginess to your whole crew – particularly those unaccustomed to the shipboard life. Habits that might seem entirely innocent ashore can be electrically extravagant at sea. It's up to you to teach them to think before they reach for that switch.

CHAPTER 10

MAINTENANCE AND TROUBLE SHOOTING

It's generally recognised that the maritime environment is tough on electrical systems. Awkward routeing, perhaps through hidden and roughly finished cavities, constant movement that can abrade and fatigue and, above all, the virtually inescapable dampness that corrodes and destroys. No one should be surprised that problems occur. The first responsibility lies with the original installer, over whom we usually have little influence. Sadly, not all builders are as conscientious as we might wish and the fact that a good proportion of any installation may be buried behind structure can be a temptation for those who would cut corners.

That said, inherited substandard practice in no way absolves us from looking after our electrics as best we can – limited though that might be. It should be the practice of all skippers to keep a weather eye on their electrical systems, ever vigilant for developing problems. A rust streak from a connection block might warn of corrosion and mounting resistance; melted insulation would signal an overload situation – potentially a serious fire hazard which should be investigated and corrected immediately. If nothing else, watchfulness will bring about a familiarity with your system that will come in very handy when it comes to sniffing out faults.

Take care of your batteries

Usually tucked out of sight, our unromantic yet crucial battery banks are often neglected. Here are some pointers to keeping them in tip-top condition and prolonging their lives.

- Inspect regularly – say, every month. Check the connections for tightness and electrolyte levels where the type allows. Top up as necessary with distilled or de-ionised water. Never add more sulphuric acid.

- Keep batteries clean. Moisture absorbed into a grimy surface can allow leakage currents. An effective cleaning fluid is a solution of baking soda and water. Then dry thoroughly. Coat the terminals in petroleum jelly (Vaseline) or silicone grease to keep moisture at bay.

- To prevent sulphation, always try and charge your batteries to full capacity – something many cheap chargers can never achieve. Never leave batteries partially discharged.

- It's helpful to keep batteries exercised. Solar panels are ideal for this. They can be safely left unattended and will keep charge levels up in your absence. They will also compensate for any 'parasitic drain' caused by permanently active systems such as alarms, automatic bilge pumps and – ironically – battery monitoring devices.

- Be honest with yourself. No matter how good the quality and how assiduously they have been maintained, batteries have finite service lives and will eventually need replacement. When the time comes, replace them.

Load test

Many batteries have a built in hydrometers (see page 23) seen externally as tiny windows which change colour to indicate charge levels. Useful though these are, they only sample a single cell so are not an indicator of overall condition. There was a time when the terminals of each cell were accessible so their voltage could be checked individually, but this is rarely possible with modern batteries.

These days it's more usual to check the general health of a battery by performing a 'load' or 'drop' test. Here's how:

- **Start with a fully or nearly charged battery which at rest should have a voltage of about 12.6 – 12.9V depending upon type and age.**

- **Switch on about 10A worth of load and wait for a few minutes. The load could made up of 5 x 25W navigation lights (about 2A each) or 12 x 10A cabin lights (0.8A each) or a mix of both.**

- **Leave them on for a few minutes then switch them off. Inevitably the battery voltage will have dropped, but the true test is how fast it recovers, so…**

- **…wait a few minutes and measure the voltage again. If the battery has bounced back to almost its original level, all is OK and you can put away your wallet. If not, it's payout time.**

The same test can be conducted using the starter motor as a load:

- **Again, start with a fully charged battery.**

- **Crank the engine for about 10-15 seconds without allowing the engine to fire – i.e. operate the stop control while it turns over. The battery voltage will drop dramatically.**

- **Wait a few minutes as before, then measure the voltage again. Draw the same conclusions from what you find.**

Of course, this test only works if you can select which battery is placed under load. Where dedicated starter and domestic batteries are fitted, determining the condition of the domestic bank might be impracticable with this last method.

CIRCUITS – TROUBLESHOOTING

Circuits vary in complexity. Some perform very simple roles – supporting a lone bilge pump for instance. Others are more complicated, with a number of related appliances (lighting circuits for lights, instrument circuits for instruments, etc) strung along their length and possibly scattered some distance apart.

Then there are the mechanical aspects. Does that inert windlass have faulty controls or supply or is it simply seized? The engine fault finding chart on page 74 illustrates the typically inextricable relationship between the invisible world of electrics and the greasy, clanking world of mechanical engineering. When things go wrong, recognising the distinction between them will determine what sort of tools you will need to make a repair.

In our introduction to multimeters on page 14 one of their most useful functions – testing electrical 'continuity' – barely got a mention. It's now time for us to examine this provision more closely since it's a vital tool in our diagnostic armoury.

Some multimeters have a dedicated continuity setting. When the probes are applied to each end of a conductor – whether a whole circuit or even a single component – a small current from a battery inside the multimeter attempts to pass through it. If the attempt is successful, a beeper sounds, telling us there are no breaks in the circuit.

Don't despair if your multimeter doesn't have a continuity setting. You can use any of the resistance ranges ( ) to check. Select a range and the figure '1' should appear in the display. This indicates infinite resistance – pretty obvious as there's no circuit. Touch the two probes together and this should be replaced by '00.0' – zero resistance. As you would expect, this most elementary of circuits is complete.

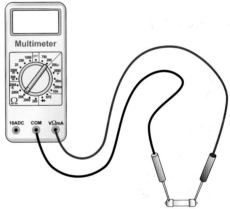

Figure 10:1 Testing continuity across a single component

You can apply this simple procedure to test the continuity across a single component – perhaps a fuse or switch – or a whole circuit. Don't expect a row of noughts always to pop up in the display, since there will always be some resistance, particularly in extended circuits. But if it seems excessive you should try and identify the cause to make sure there isn't a faulty connection somewhere.

> **!** **WARNING: Never attempt to measure resistance or conduct a continuity test on a live circuit. The multimeter relies on its own power source and a powerful external supply will probably blow its fuse. And don't forget to isolate solar panels and wind generators! These are often overlooked.**

To put this subject in a practical setting, let's assume a malfunctioning engine start circuit and see how we might use a multimeter to chase down the problem. It might help to extend the negative (–) lead so, where appropriate, it can be connected to the engine block or other convenient ground, allowing you to wander about with the meter in your hand.

After checking that the main isolating switch is switched 'ON', proceed as follows, starting at the battery:

■ Select the 20V DC range and measure the battery voltage between the battery posts (1). The voltage should be at least 12V.

ACTION: *Charge battery if necessary.*

■ Now shift the probes to the terminals (2) that connect the cables to the posts. If the voltage is noticeably lower, one or both of the connections must be suspect.

ACTION: *Remove terminals, clean all connecting surfaces and reassemble. At this time also check the negative (ground) connection to the engine block. Vibration could have loosened it.*

■ Check the voltage first at (3) then on the other side of the isolation/selector switch, which of course must be 'ON', at (4). There should be very little difference. A voltage drop would signal a defective switch or poor connections.

ACTION: *Remake connections. If the problem persists replace the switch.*

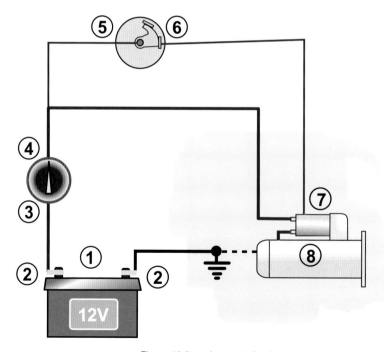

Figure 10:2 engine start check

■ Check the voltage at (5). If OK....

■ ...move the probe to the output (solenoid) side of the starter switch or button (6) and operate switch. The full voltage should be apparent. Again, if it isn't, this is likely to be a problem with either the connections or the switch. Key type switches are notoriously fallible so expect the worst.

ACTION: *These are sealed units with no internal access. Replacement is the only option.*

■ Check voltage at (7). If OK ...

■ Turn the switch 'ON' again and check the voltage at (8). If the solenoid (which acts as a switch to summon up the large current needed by the starter motor) is working properly this should show a healthy voltage. If not, the problem lies inside the relay. Either the solenoid coil is malfunctioning or the heavy duty contact points have been eroded away (see Fig 10:3).

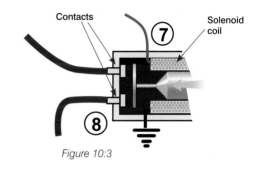

Figure 10:3

ACTION: *You could check the coil by running a continuity test on it (remember to switch the power 'OFF'). It should show a low resistance. But this is fairly academic, since it's now time to call in the professionals. Except one last possibility ...*

■ Check that the starter motor unit is securely mounted. The negative return needed to complete the circuit is via the metal casing. If the motor has vibrated loose, the connection may not be good enough.

Emergency engine starting

If, in the course of these various tests, you find the starter switch to be faulty, you can bypass it by bridging across the two smaller terminals on the end of the solenoid with a screwdriver or similar (Figure: 10:4).

Still no luck? Then the solenoid itself is probably the culprit, in which case you can try supplying power to the starter motor directly, this time by bridging across the two larger terminals as shown in Figure 10:5. A lot of current will be conducted so expect some spectacular arcing. And be careful not to touch any surrounding metalwork with the screwdriver blade, since this will produce a dead short circuit.

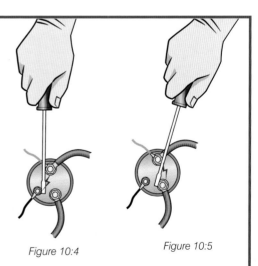

Figure 10:4

Figure 10:5

Problems starting engines can plague us all at some time or other. But is the fault electrical or mechanical? The most sensible course of action is to take a holistic approach as described here:

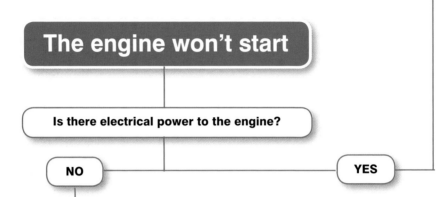

The engine won't start

Is there electrical power to the engine?

NO   **YES**

1) Is the battery isolation switch 'On'?

2) Check for blown fuse or tripped circuit breaker

3) Is the battery totally discharged?

4) Are the battery terminal leads connected?

5) Is the battery earth lead to the engine block connected and secure?

1) This is a common but surprisingly easy mistake to make. The usual arrangement is to have a single switch in the positive side of the circuit, but many European boats also isolate the negative side. Both must be switched on for the engine to start.

2) Engine control fuses aren't always easy to find. There may be a small fuse box mounted on the engine block somewhere or – a ridiculous practice on some engines – it could even be wound in beneath the engine wiring loom insulation! You may have to consult the service manual.

3) A battery's voltage doesn't have to be zero for it to be useless. A fully charged 12V battery at rest will show around 12.8V. By the time that reading drops to 10.5V it's effectively 100% flat. If your power management system includes a voltmeter or bar graph type state-of-charge indicator, monitoring the battery condition is very straightforward. If not, you will have to resort to a hydrometer or portable multimeter.

4) Engine starting creates high electrical demands. Any voltage drop due to corroded or loose connections can result in total failure. Check that there's no corrosion and that the terminal clamps are tight on the posts.

5) The same goes for the cable that goes from the battery negative to the engine block. Vibration can easily loosen the connection, so make sure it's clean and nip up the securing bolt.

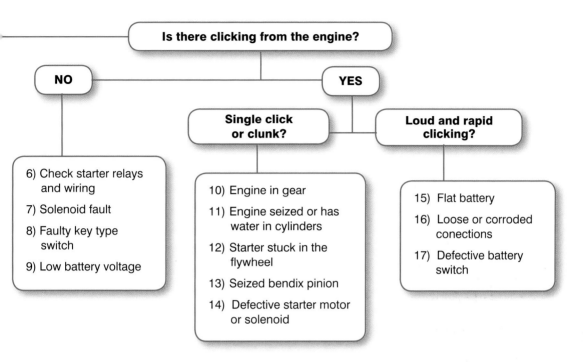

6) Starter solenoids can draw quite a lot of power. To avoid running heavy cables from the starting switch to the solenoid, a secondary switch known as a 'relay' is often used. Turning the ignition key activates the relay which, in turn, switches on the power to operate the solenoid. Relays are unserviceable items. If defective they should be replaced.

7) Solenoids sometimes get stuck. They can often be freed by tapping them lightly with the power on. Lightly, mind: DON'T CLOUT IT HARD WITH A HAMMER!

8) Key type switches are notoriously prone to faults. Pushbutton ones are much more reliable. The switch can be bypassed by connecting across the solenoid terminals.

9) If your cabin lights dim when you operate the starting switch, you can be sure that batteries are at a low state of charge. Try switching off all other appliances so the starter motor can have what little power is left.

10) Most engines will start in gear but if the prop is heavily fouled there may be too much resistance.

11) If the water has only been in the engine a short time, you can act to prevent expensive damage. If it has seized, you are almost certainly facing a complete overhaul.

12, 13 & 14) The starter motor should be removed so it can be freed up or sent away for repair.

15) If the engine can't be hand started, there's nothing for it but to find some other means of charging the battery.

16) Clean and tighten as required.

17) Bypass or replace.

An electrical device not working?

Usually the first clue you get that something is wrong is when an appliance isn't working or not functioning normally. Sometimes the cause is obvious – a blackened lamp, for example, that can easily be replaced. Other faults may call for some simple diagnostic tests.

Here are some steps you can take:

■ Is the input voltage to the distribution panel OK? Remember that at about 11.7V a battery is effectively discharged; at 10.6V it's dead.

■ Are all devices on the same circuit defective or is it just one? For example if your chart plotter is active but the back-up GPS isn't, then this is clearly a localised problem involving the latter.

ACTION: *Check connections and fuses – including any inline or internal fuses. Activate the circuit and, with your multimeter set to the appropriate DC voltage range, measure the battery voltage and that of the power supply at the device (Figure 10:6). If a large voltage drop is found, the device may not be defective at all but may have shut itself down deliberately as a preventative measure against producing corrupted information. Follow the supply circuit looking for a faulty connection. A zero reading means there must be a break in the cable.*

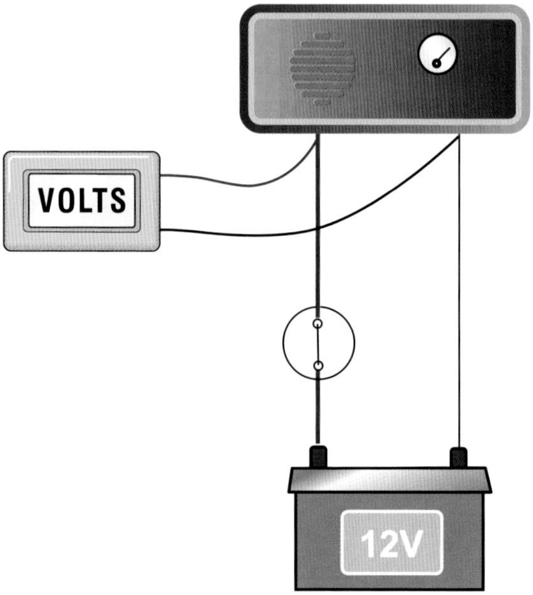

■ If a whole circuit is down, you should suspect a problem on or close to the distribution panel.

Fig 10:6 *Check the power supply at the load first. If that's OK the equipment must be faulty.*

ACTION: *Check fuses and circuit breakers and all relevant connections – including the negative returns which could be by way of bus cables. In the latter case, other circuits could also be compromised – a useful clue to the cause.*

Electrical faults are usually very simple in themselves but can be elusive to find. Always work methodically. Remember that cables can break unseen so you must be prepared to conduct continuity tests a section at a time.

Faults out of reach?

It's in the nature of boats that some equipment isn't easy to get at – lights up the mast being an obvious example. But that doesn't mean they can't be tested.

Set the multimeter to test continuity – beep or setting – and apply it to the circuit as shown in Figure 10:7 – or at the deck plugs, if any, a common source of faults. Expect some resistance since there's a lamp in the circuit but it should not be excessive. Infinite resistance means a break in the circuit so the next step is to visually inspect all connections before … climbing the mast to replace the lamp!

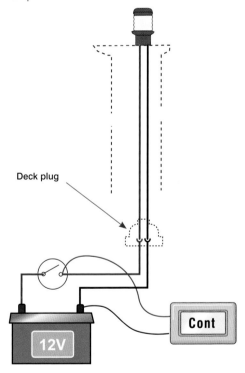

Deck plug

Cont

12V

Fig 10:7 Check the circuit continuity from the switch. If found to be faulty, check again at the deck plug.

Electrical tools:

This list assumes that a selection of 'standard' tools (such as screwdrivers, spanners, pliers etc) are already on board.

- Multimeter – preferably the digital type.
- Needle nosed pliers. These are more delicate than the regular type.
- Crimping tool(s).
- Small screwdrivers.
- Side cutters for cutting cable neatly.
- Polarity tester.
- Wire strippers and crimpers. Ideally, these should be separate tools but the less expensive combined type will do at a pinch.
- Test light – often sold with a small screwdriver as a probe.
- Hydrometer – only if you have flooded lead acid batteries.
- Butane fuelled or 12V soldering iron.
- Electric heat gun (for shore power use).

SPARES AND MATERIALS

- Spare fuses – at least one for every size, type and rating on board.
- Crimp connectors in a variety of sizes and connection types.
- Heat shrink tape, adhesive lined type.
- Insulating tape.
- Self-amalgamating tape.
- Cable ties – various sizes and lengths.
- Petroleum jelly and/or silicone grease.
- De-ionised water (for topping up liquid lead acid batteries).

Hunting down DC leakage currents

Stray currents produced by electrical leakages can occur almost anywhere. But the most susceptible areas are the bilge and engine spaces where heat can break down insulation and damp surfaces can provide conductive pathways to ground. Start by looking for obvious problems – some can be glaring. On one boat the chocolate block type connection to the pump was actually immersed in bilge water. On another, an engine hatch had pinched a wire, a single bare strand now touching foil-covered sound insulation.

Work methodically, following all suspicious circuits as far as you can along their lengths. If a visual inspection yields nothing, you will need to run some tests. Here's the recommended procedure.

Each individual DC distribution circuit must be tested in turn, so all other circuits should be deactivated by opening their CBs. Next, connect your multimeter so it forms part of the circuit as shown in Figures 10:8 and 10:9. Set it to read amps at the highest range your meter will allow – typically 10A.

TO TEST THE POSITIVE LEAD:
Make sure its circuit breaker is closed (i.e. the circuit is ON). The equipment it serves should be switched OFF. If the multimeter shows zero amps, drop to the next lower range, then the next and so on until a reading appears. Anything approaching 10mA means it's bad news. There's a significant leak in the positive side of the circuit that must be traced by checking one component at a time.

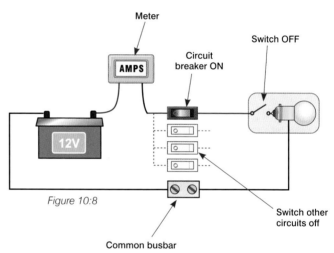

Figure 10:8

TO TEST THE NEGATIVE LEAD: Leave the breaker ON and also switch the equipment ON. Disconnect the negative wire from the common bus bar. With the multimeter, follow the same procedure as before, drawing the same conclusions from whatever you find.

If necessary, check the other circuits in similar manner.

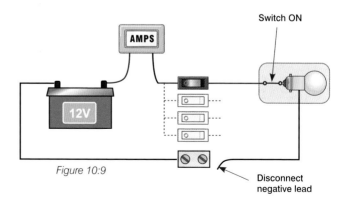

Figure 10:9

POWER CONSUMPTION TABLE

Device	Amps (at 12V)	Underway (hrs)	Ah	Anchor (hrs)	Ah
Tricolour light (25W)	2.10	10	21.00		
Anchor light (10W)	0.90			10	9.00
Running lights (bicolour & stern)*	5.00				
Masthead (steaming) light*	0.9				
Deck lights	1.70	0.25	0.43		
Cockpit light	1.00			4	4.00
Cabin lights (typical usage total)			3.00		15.00
Chart table light	0.30	2	0.60		
Autopilot (50% usage)*	2.00	12	24.00		
Radar (transmit)	2.50	2	5.00		
Radar (standby)	1.00	10	10.00		
VHF (transmit)	1.20	1	1.20	1	1.20
VHF (standby)	0.30	24	7.20	24	7.20
GPS (with use of anchor alarm)	0.40	24	9.60	24	9.60
Sailing instruments	0.30	24	7.20		
Navtex receiver	0.40	24	9.60	24	9.60
Stereo	0.90	2	1.80	6	10.80
Refrigerator (20min per hour)	4.00	8	32.00	8	32.00
Watermaker	8.00	1.5	12.00	1.5	12.00
Gas alarm	0.15	24	3.60	24	3.60
Distribution panel monitor	0.10	24	2.40	24	2.40
Windlass (average usage 800W)*	67.00			0.25	16.75
			150.63		**133.15**

* Either wholly or usually used under power with the alternator serving at least part of the demand.

CABLE SIZES

To avoid unacceptable voltage drops and the possibility of overheating, it's very important that electrical cables be large enough to carry the loads placed on them (see page 44). The tables here show the minimum cross sectional conductor area required (in square millimetres) for different currents and circuit lengths – the latter being the length from the distribution panel and back again. The colours indicate the equivalent American Wire Gauge (AWG) sizes which are widely available in the UK and beyond.

Cable length (metres)

Current (amps)	2	4	6	8	10	15	20	25	30	35	40	45	50
1	0.09	0.18	0.27	0.36	0.46	0.68	0.91	1.14	1.37	1.59	1.82	2.05	2.28
2	0.18	0.36	0.55	0.73	0.91	1.37	1.82	2.28	2.73	3.19	3.64	4.10	4.56
3	0.27	0.55	0.82	1.09	1.37	2.05	2.73	3.42	4.10	4.78	5.47	6.15	6.83
4	0.36	0.73	1.09	1.46	1.82	2.73	3.64	4.56	5.47	6.38	7.29	8.20	9.11
5	0.46	0.91	1.37	1.82	2.28	3.42	4.56	5.69	6.83	7.97	9.11	10.25	11.38
6	0.55	1.09	1.64	2.19	2.73	4.10	5.47	6.83	8.20	9.57	10.93	12.30	13.67
7	0.64	1.28	1.91	2.55	3.19	4.78	6.38	7.97	9.57	11.16	12.76	14.35	15.94
8	0.73	1.46	2.19	2.92	3.64	5.47	7.29	9.11	10.93	12.76	14.58	16.40	18.22
9	0.82	1.64	2.46	3.28	4.10	6.15	8.20	10.25	12.30	14.35	16.40	18.45	20.50
10	0.91	1.82	2.73	3.64	4.56	6.83	9.11	11.39	13.67	15.94	18.22	20.50	22.78
11	1.00	2.00	3.01	4.01	5.01	7.52	10.02	12.53	15.03	17.54	20.04	22.55	25.06
12	1.09	2.19	3.28	4.37	5.47	8.20	10.93	13.67	16.40	19.13	21.87	24.60	27.33
13	1.18	2.37	3.55	4.74	5.92	8.88	11.84	14.81	17.77	20.73	23.69	26.65	29.61
14	1.28	2.55	3.83	5.10	6.38	9.57	12.76	15.94	19.13	22.32	25.51	28.70	31.89
15	1.37	2.73	4.10	5.47	6.83	10.25	13.67	17.08	20.50	23.92	27.33	30.75	34.17
16	1.46	2.92	4.37	5.83	7.29	10.93	14.58	18.22	21.87	25.51	29.16	32.80	36.44
17	1.55	3.10	4.65	6.20	7.74	11.62	15.49	19.36	23.23	27.11	30.98	34.85	38.72
18	1.64	3.28	4.92	6.56	8.20	12.30	16.40	20.50	24.60	28.70	32.80	36.90	41.00
19	1.73	3.46	5.19	6.92	8.66	12.98	17.31	21.64	25.97	30.29	34.62	38.95	43.28
20	1.82	3.64	5.47	7.29	9.11	13.67	18.22	22.78	27.33	31.89	36.44	41.00	45.56
25	2.28	4.56	6.83	9.11	11.39	17.08	22.78	28.47	34.17	39.86	45.56	51.25	
30	2.73	5.47	8.20	10.93	13.67	20.50	27.33	34.17	41.00	47.83			
35	3.19	6.38	9.57	12.76	15.94	23.92	31.89	39.86	47.83				
40	3.64	7.29	10.93	14.58	18.22	27.33	36.44	45.56					
45	4.10	8.20	12.30	16.40	20.50	30.75	41.00	51.25					
50	4.56	9.11	13.67	18.22	22.78	34.17	45.56						
55	5.01	10.02	15.03	20.04	25.06	37.58	50.11						
60	5.47	10.93	16.40	21.87	27.33	41.00							
65	5.92	11.84	17.77	23.69	29.61	44.41							
70	6.38	12.76	19.13	25.51	31.89	47.83							
75	6.83	13.67	20.50	27.33	34.17	51.25							
80	7.29	14.58	21.87	29.16	36.44								
85	7.74	15.49	23.23	30.98	38.72								
90	8.20	16.40	24.60	32.80	41.00								
95	8.66	17.31	25.97	34.62	43.28								
100	9.11	18.22	27.33	36.44	45.56								

Voltage drop 3%

AWG

18
16
14
12
10
8
6
4
2
1
1/0

Cable length (metres)

Current (amps)	2	4	6	8	10	15	20	25	30	35	40	45	50
1	0.03	0.05	0.08	0.11	0.14	0.21	0.27	0.34	0.41	0.48	0.55	0.62	0.68
2	0.05	0.11	0.16	0.22	0.27	0.41	0.55	0.68	0.82	0.96	1.09	1.23	1.37
3	0.08	0.16	0.25	0.33	0.41	0.62	0.82	1.03	1.23	1.44	1.64	1.85	2.05
4	0.11	0.22	0.33	0.44	0.55	0.82	1.09	1.37	1.64	1.91	2.19	2.46	2.73
5	0.14	0.27	0.41	0.55	0.68	1.03	1.37	1.71	2.05	2.39	2.73	3.08	3.42
6	0.16	0.33	0.49	0.66	0.82	1.23	1.64	2.05	2.46	2.87	3.28	3.69	4.10
7	0.19	0.38	0.57	0.77	0.96	1.44	1.91	2.39	2.87	3.35	3.83	4.31	4.78
8	0.22	0.44	0.66	0.87	1.09	1.64	2.19	2.73	3.28	3.83	4.37	4.92	5.47
9	0.25	0.49	0.74	0.98	1.23	1.85	2.46	3.08	3.69	4.31	4.92	5.54	6.15
10	0.27	0.55	0.82	1.09	1.37	2.05	2.73	3.42	4.10	4.78	5.47	6.15	6.83
11	0.30	0.60	0.90	1.20	1.50	2.26	3.01	3.76	4.51	5.26	6.01	6.77	7.52
12	0.33	0.66	0.98	1.31	1.64	2.46	3.28	4.10	4.92	5.74	6.56	7.38	
13	0.36	0.71	1.07	1.42	1.78	2.67	3.55	4.44	5.33	6.22	7.11		
14	0.38	0.77	1.15	1.53	1.91	2.87	3.83	4.78	5.74	6.70	7.65		
15	0.41	0.82	1.23	1.64	2.05	3.08	4.10	5.13	6.15	7.18			
16	0.44	0.87	1.31	1.75	2.19	3.28	4.37	5.47	6.56	7.65			
17	0.46	0.93	1.39	1.86	2.32	3.49	4.65	5.81	6.97				
18	0.49	0.98	1.48	1.97	2.46	3.69	4.92	6.15	7.38				
19	0.52	1.04	1.56	2.08	2.60	3.90	5.19	6.49	7.79				
20	0.55	1.09	1.64	2.19	2.73	4.10	5.47	6.83					13.67
25	0.68	1.37	2.05	2.73	3.42	5.13	6.83				13.67	15.38	17.08
30	0.82	1.64	2.46	3.28	4.10	6.15				14.35	16.40	18.45	20.50
35	0.96	1.91	2.87	3.83	4.78	7.18			14.35	16.74	19.13	21.53	23.92
40	1.09	2.19	3.28	4.37	5.47			13.67	16.40	19.13	21.87	24.60	27.33
45	1.23	2.46	3.69	4.92	6.15			15.38	18.45	21.53	24.60	27.68	30.75
50	1.37	2.73	4.10	5.47	6.83		13.67	17.08	20.50	23.92	27.33	30.75	34.17
55	1.50	3.01	4.51	6.01	7.52		15.03	18.79	22.55	26.31	30.07	33.83	37.58
60	1.64	3.28	4.92	6.56			16.40	20.50	24.60	28.70	32.80	36.90	41.00
65	1.78	3.55	5.33	7.11		13.33	17.77	22.21	26.65	31.09	35.53	39.98	44.42
70	1.91	3.83	5.74	7.65		14.35	19.13	23.92	28.70	33.48	38.27	43.05	47.83
75	2.05	4.10	6.15			15.38	20.50	25.63	30.75	35.88	41.00	46.13	51.25
80	2.19	4.37	6.56			16.40	21.87	27.33	32.80	38.27	43.73	49.20	
85	2.32	4.65	6.97			17.43	23.23	29.04	34.85	40.66	46.47	52.28	
90	2.46	4.92	7.38			18.45	24.60	30.75	36.90	43.05	49.20		
95	2.60	5.19	7.79			19.48	25.97	32.46	38.95	45.44	51.93		
100	2.73	5.47			13.67	20.50	27.33	34.17	41.00	47.83			

AWG

18
16
14
12
10
8
4
2
1
1/0

Voltage drop 10%

Absorption charge	The second charging stage of a multi-stage charge regime.
Alternating current (AC)	A form of electricity that reverses direction at regular intervals.
Alternator	An electrical generator that produces an alternating current.
Amp Hour (Ah)	One amp hour is equal to one amp of current flowing for one hour.
Ampere (amp)	An ampere is the unit of electrical current flow.
Anode	The electrode through which a current enters an electrolyte.
Battery	A device for storing electricity by means of chemical processes.
Battery combiner	A device that connects two or more batteries in parallel once a certain charge level has been reached.
Bulk charge	The first charging stage of a multi-stage charge regime.
Circuit breaker	A safety device that detects excessive power demands and switches off automatically.
Current	The movement of electrons through a conductor.
Dezincification	A galvanic process affecting brass alloys where the zinc is eroded.
Diode	A sort of one-way valve for electricity. Current can only flow in one direction.
Direct current (DC)	The type of electricity we draw from our batteries. Current flows in one direction.
Electrolysis	A process by which chemically bonded compounds are seperated by the passage of an electric current.
Electrolyte	The liquid inside storage batteries. A conductive medium.
Float charge	The third charging stage in a multi-stage charge regime. Maintains battery charge levels.
Fuse	A conductor - often encapsulated - designed to melt if overheated by an excessive current.
Galvanic	Electrical interaction between different metals immersed in an electrolyte.
Generator	A device for producing an electric current.
Hydrometer	An instrument for measuring specific gravity. Used to measure battery charge state.
Inductive loads	Loads that produce a magnetic field - often accompanied by heat.
Inverter	An electrical device for converting DC to AC power.
Ion	An atom either missing or having an extra electron.

Kilovolt-Amp (kVA)	Unit commonly used to rate generators.
Kilowatt (kW)	One thousand watts of electricity.
Light emitting diode (LED)	Type of lighting having very low power consumption.
Load	Any device that consumes electricity.
Modified sine wave	An AC waveform that approximates a sine wave in a series of steps.
Multimeter	An instrument for measuring various electrical values - volts, amps and ohms being typical.
Oscillator	An electro-mechanical device for converting DC to AC.
Oscilloscope	An instrument that provides a visual display of a wave form.
Parallel circuit	A group of devices wired together so voltage remains constant and current varies.
Photon	Think of it as a particle of light.
Photovoltaic	A device for converting light into electricity.
Primary cell	A battery where the chemical changes are irreversible.
Rectifier	A device for converting AC into DC.
Residual current device (RCD)	A safety device which detects an imbalance between live and neutral wires and trips if one occurs.
Resistance	Any opposition to the flow of current.
Resistive loads	Loads resulting purely from resistance.
Secondary cells	Batteries where the chemical changes can be reversed - i.e. rechargeable.
Semi-conductor	Conductors with a limited capacity to carry electricity.
Series circuit	A group of devices wired together like beads on a necklace. Amps remain constant but voltage varies.
Sine wave	A smooth output waveform going above and below zero. The output from top quality inverters.
Solenoid	An electro-magnet in the form of a tunnel.
Specific gravity	The density of a substance relative to fresh water.
Splitting diode	A device that divides a charging current so it can charge more that one battery.
Volt	A unit describing the amount of electrical force.
Watt	A unit describing the measure of electrical power.

RYA *Membership*

Promoting and Protecting Boating
www.rya.org.uk

RYA Membership

The RYA is the national organisation which represents the interests of everyone who goes boating for pleasure.

The greater the membership, the louder our voice when it comes to protecting members' interests.

Apply for membership today, and support the RYA, to help the RYA support you.

BENEFITS OF MEMBERSHIP

- Special members' discounts on a range of products and services including boat insurance, books, charts, DVD's and class certificates
- Access to expert advice on all aspects of boating from legal wrangles to training matters
- Free issue of Certificates of Competence, increasingly asked for by everyone from overseas governments to holiday companies, insurance underwriters to boat hirers
- Access to the wide range of RYA publications,including the quarterly magazine
- Third Party insurance for windsurfing members
- Free Internet access with RYA-Online
- Special discounts on AA membership
- Regular offers in RYA Magazine
- ...and much more

JOIN NOW

Membership form opposite or join online at www.rya.org.uk

Visit our website for information, advice, members' services and web shop.

1 **Important** To help us comply with Data Protection legislation, please tick *either* Box A or Box B (you must tick Box A to ensure you receive the full benefits of RYA membership). The RYA will not pass your data to third parties.

☐ **A.** I wish to join the RYA and receive future information on member services, benefits and offers by post and email.

☐ **B.** I wish to join the RYA but do not wish to receive future information on member services, benefits and offers by post and email.

When completed, please send this form to: RYA, RYA House, Ensign Way, Hamble, Southampton, SO31 4YA

2

Title	Forename	Surname	Date of Birth		Male	Female
			D D / M M / Y Y		☐	☐
1.						
2.			D D / M M / Y Y		☐	☐
3.			D D / M M / Y Y		☐	☐
4.			D D / M M / Y Y		☐	☐

Address

Town   County

Evening Telephone   Daytime Telephone

Post Code

email

Signature: ....   Date: ....

3 **Type of membership required:** *(Tick Box)*

☐ *Personal*   *Annual rate £39 or £36 by Direct Debit*

☐ *Under 21*   *Annual rate £13 (no reduction for Direct Debit)*

☐ *Family**   *Annual rate £58 or £55 by Direct Debit*

* *Family Membership: 2 adults plus any under 21s all living at the same address*

4 Please tick ONE box to show your main boating interest.

☐ Yacht Racing   ☐ Yacht Cruising
☐ Dinghy Racing   ☐ Dinghy Cruising
☐ Personal Watercraft   ☐ Inland Waterways
☐ Powerboat Racing   ☐ Windsurfing
☐ Motor Boating   ☐ Sportsboats and RIBs

Please see Direct Debit form overleaf

Instructions to your Bank or Building Society to pay by Direct Debit

Please complete this form and return it to:
Royal Yachting Association, RYA House, Ensign Way, Hamble, Southampton, Hampshire SO31 4YA

DIRECT Debit

1. To The Manager: _____ Bank/Building Society

Address: _____

_____

Post Code: _____

2. Name(s) of account holder(s)

_____

_____

3. Branch Sort Code

☐ ☐ — ☐ ☐ — ☐ ☐

4. Bank or Building Society account number

☐ ☐ ☐ ☐ ☐ ☐ ☐ ☐

Originators Identification Number

9	5	5	2	1	3

5. RYA Membership Number (For office use only)

_____

6. Instruction to pay your Bank or Building Society

Please pay Royal Yachting Association Direct Debits from the account detailed in this instruction subject to the safeguards assured by The Direct Debit Guarantee.
I understand that this instruction may remain with the Royal Yachting Association and, if so, details will be passed electronically to my Bank/Building Society.

Signature(s) _____

Date _____

Banks and Building Societies may not accept Direct Debit instructions for some types of account

---

Cash, Cheque, Postal Order enclosed £ _____
Made payable to the Royal Yachting Association

077 **Office use only:** Membership Number Allocated _____

Office use / Centre Stamp

Join The Green Blue...

...in protecting our coasts and waterways.

Each time we use, clean or maintain our boat we may be harming the beautiful environment we are out to enjoy. The good news is that it there are simple things everyone can do to prevent this. Follow our 'top tips' to ensure that your conscience is as clean as your boat!

EFFECTS ON WILDLIFE
Find out whether the areas you visit are protected and why. There may be vulnerable seabed species, so beware of dragging your anchor.

OIL AND FUEL SPILLS
Good maintenance of fuel lines, connections and seals helps avoid leaks. Check bilge water for contaminants before routine pumping.

ANTIFOULING & MARINE PAINTS
Only scrub off the fouling, not the paint and encourage your marina, club or boatyard to collect & properly dispose of wash down residues.

WASTE MANAGEMENT
Don't throw anything over the side, including food; even orange peel can take up to 2 years to decompose in the water.

RESOURCE EFFICIENCY
The latest generation of wind generators are quiet, efficient and a great way to charge your batteries.

CLEANING AND MAINTENANCE
Replacing acidic teak cleaners with a mild soap and abrasive pad is not only better for the environment but eliminates solvents which may damage seam compounds.

More tips and advice can be found on our website: www.thegreenblue.org.uk

Read the Environmental Code of Practice to find out how your club can reduce its impact on the environment: www.ecop.org.uk

**THE GREEN BLUE
RYA House, Ensign Way, Hamble, Southampton
SO31 4YA
Tel: 023 8060 4227
www.thegreenblue.org.uk
info@thegreenblue.org.uk
© Copyright The Green Blue 2007**

THE CROWN ESTATE

RYA Training Courses

for all ages, abilities and aspirations

Get the most from your time on the water with our range of practical and shorebased courses.

Also, a whole range of navigation and specialis short courses:

> **BASIC NAVIGATION AND SAFETY**

> **DAY SKIPPER**

> **COASTAL SKIPPER/ YACHTMASTER® OFFSHORE**

> **YACHTMASTER® OCEAN**

> **DIESEL ENGINE**

> **OFFSHORE SAFETY**

> **VHF RADIO**

> **RADAR**

> **SEA SURVIVAL**

> **FIRST AID**

Sail cruising from the beginners' Start Yachting course to Yachtmaster®

Sailing Away School of Sailing

Motor cruising from the introductory Helmsman's course to Yachtmaster®

Graham Snook/MBM

RYA

For further information see www.ryatraining.org, call 00 44 (0)23 8060 4158 for a brochure or email training@rya.org.uk

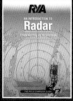